The Incredible Mrs. Chadwick

THE MOST NOTORIOUS WOMAN

OF HER AGE

The Incredible Mrs. Chadwick

THE MOST NOTORIOUS WOMAN OF HER AGE

by

JOHN S. CROSBIE

McGRAW-HILL RYERSON LIMITED
Toronto   Montreal   New York

1 2 3 4 5 6 7 8 9 0 D 4 3 2 1 0 9 8 7 6 5

ISBN 0-07-082194-1

Printed and bound in Canada

This book is gratefully dedicated
to my wife Patty, who first
drew Betsy to my attention.

FOREWORD

This book has been built as a monument to Betsy Bigley, a remarkable woman. It would be superficial to say of her that, having extracted millions of dollars from people on false pretences, she was one of the greatest swindlers that the world has ever known. There was much more to her than that statement alone suggests.

On the pages that follow you will find her story set out as fairly and accurately as we have been able to reconstruct it. So little is known of her early years that I have dared to guess what kind of childhood would produce such a woman, using, I hope, the kind of inventiveness of which Betsy would have been proud. However, once her story begins to carry her past the age of thirteen, away from home and on to become world-renowned as Cassie L. Chadwick, there has been little need to do more than let actual events unfold.

This we have done by drawing on old newspaper files and articles and such other sources as a book published in 1905 by the Laning Company (New York ?). This collection of press clippings, arranged in roughly chronological order and covering the peak of her fame, bears the impressively long title of "The History and Story of the Doings of the Famous Cassie L. Chadwick the So-Called 'Queen of Finance' Showing How She Fleeced the Bankers As Told By the Press During the Period of Her Exposure, Negotiation, Arrest and Imprisonment In Jail."

Betsy was born in Canada halfway through the nineteenth century and lived on into the early twentieth. In those decades, North American women were expected to be demure homemakers, to subordinate themselves to the male ego and, above all, to stay out of the business world.

Apparently, no one thought to tell Betsy.

The Incredible Mrs. Chadwick

THE MOST NOTORIOUS WOMAN

OF HER AGE

CHAPTER ONE

The frog accidentally came apart. It wasn't Betsy's fault but it certainly made a mess of her pinafore. She knew that when she and Alice and Mary and Emily got back to the house the kindly old lady who pretended to be their mother (but was really a gypsy princess who had stolen them as babies) would be very upset.

Gathering her sisters around, Betsy placed the messy remains on a boulder and held a funeral service. Using the manner of their minister—an earnest Anglican who, one assumed, had been exposed at some point in his youth to a group of travelling actors—Betsy delivered an oration.

". . . And as one looks back on the life of this wonderful creature," she declaimed, pointing down dramatically at the corpse, "one can only be surprised that so great and good a life should end so sadly. Why? Why, I ask you, did this poor animal come apart? I will tell you, my friends. I will tell you." She leaned across the pulpit of the boulder toward her rapt if limited audience, and her voice fell to a projected whisper. "He came apart, dear children of God, because he was in love! Where else in all the world can you find a greater example of love than this?" Her volume rose as she straightened up and flung wide her arms. "Look! Look, all of you! See this blood! See these stains! Here is proof—proof of his great love. So great a love that he, poor soul, could not contain it. You have heard, as I have, of people whose hearts were bursting with sadness. Here I show you the power of love. A love so great and so strong that the whole frog burst!"

Her congregation, forgetting the solemnity of the occasion, broke into admiring applause. But she quickly brought them back into line with a dramatic, warning gesture.

"Wait! Stop and think, all of you! Suppose that all the world found out! Suppose that evil people—and the world is full of evil people, my friends—suppose they heard from you of this power of love. Just think! They would go around stirring up love, great love like this—and pretty soon there would be frogs bursting all over the place. And not just frogs, my friends, but horses and cows, and even people! We must do something, my friends. We must save the world from this. How? By swearing to take this secret knowledge with us to our graves! Do you all swear?"

The congregation nodded vigorously. But Alice, who was only a year younger than Betsy and sometimes showed it by being distressingly practical, asked, "Yes, but what about your dress? You're going to get it when we get home!"

Betsy raised her arms and intoned, "The Lord giveth and the Lord taketh away." She pointed to the little nearby stream from which the late lamented had so unfortunately hopped into Eternity. "Come my friends, we must wash away our sins!" She began to walk toward the water. Her audience followed. "Let us descend into the water and give it our secret to hold!" When she reached the bank she kept walking. As the water reached her waist, she turned. Her sisters had faltered in their faith and were still on dry land.

"Do we all have to come in?" asked Mary.

"No," Betsy assured them, "where two or more are gathered together, it is enough for me to get wet." She began to rinse the blood out of her pinafore.

"But what are you going to tell Mother when we get home?" Alice asked.

Betsy surveyed her followers solemnly. "The secret we have this day discovered must be forever hidden from the world." Looking down with some satisfaction at the now stain-free cloth that clung to her, she smiled sweetly and said softly— certain of support—"We'll just tell her I fell in!"

The Bigley home was the only one in the Eastwood area where dinner was at night. The other families had supper, with the heavy meal served at noon. But because Betsy's father spent most days away from the house from breakfast to dark, the noon meal was light and casual. (Indeed, if her father's work as a dollar-a-day section boss on the Great Western Railway required him to be away for several days, as sometimes happened, all of the meals became pretty light and casual, for Mrs. Bigley was not a woman to wear herself down with extra effort.)

When the four sisters got home from the stream, Mrs. Bigley was waiting for them. Alice was needed to peel vegetables; Betsy had to fetch water from the well; Mary had to set the table; and Emily, well, all that Mrs. Bigley wanted from Emily Butterfingers was to stay out of the way and to try and not get stepped on.

Her instructions were poured out so quickly that she didn't

notice Betsy's clothing. It was only when Bill, her eldest son, coming in from milking the cow, encountered Betsy at the well and asked too loudly what had happened that Annie Bigley really looked at her daughter.

"My God in heaven, Betsy! What have you been into now?"

"Oh, Mummy!" Betsy sobbed, brushing past her brother and wrapping her wet arms around her mother's waist, "it was awful! We were walking along the bank looking for flowers to bring you when suddenly we heard the most terrible growl. Something was coming after us!"

"What was it?" asked her mother, always the innocent straight man.

"We don't know, do we?" asked Betsy turning to the other girls. They shook their heads, fully aware that in doing so they were telling the truth. "It looked like a big dog or something. Maybe it was a wolf." (Betsy couldn't decide whether it should be a wolf or a mad dog. She voted quickly for the wolf as being more believable.) "He came along the bank so fast we didn't know what to do for a second. Then I yelled for the others to run for their lives. I stood and faced the wolf, waving my arms to keep his attention away from the others. Then, when he was so close that I could see his fangs and the white spit flying from his mouth, I threw myself in the water. He stood on the bank and barked at me but he was afraid to come in. I kept very quiet and after a time he got tired of waiting and went away. We never saw him again."

Annie Bigley stroked her daughter's hair. "You poor, brave girl! How typical of you to want to save your sisters! But you took an awful risk, darling. You must promise me never to be so foolish again."

"But Mummy," protested Betsy, "if I hadn't done it, the

4

wolf would have eaten them all up, and then who would I have had to play with?" Emily started to giggle. Mary gave her a warning nudge.

Annie glared at her youngest. "It's not the least bit funny, Emily! Now, you take Betsy's pail and get that water in here. Betsy, dear, I think you should take off your wet things and lie down for a while before dinner."

"Yes, Mummy," said Betsy meekly. "I do feel a little faint." Bill snorted, but then Bill always snorted. Unlike his sisters, he did not like to play pretend and had long since given up trying to understand what was real and what was unreal in the fast-changing world of Betsy's mind. As she made her heroine's exit from the kitchen, he turned his mind back to the things he knew and understood and began to pour the milk into the separator.

By train time Betsy was considered rested enough to go meet her father. It was the one event of the day that nothing, even a wolf, would have kept her from enjoying. On the days when he was either home farming or too far down the line to get back, she moped through her dinner. But on those wonderful occasions when the train would come puffing along the track with him standing on the rear platform, she would be waiting at the little Eastwood station, jumping up and down with excitement, eager to grasp his big hand and start the walk home.

As they strolled along the buggy-rutted road, he would tell her what he had seen since he left. Perhaps a private car had gone through with a big, important-looking man sitting at the window puffing a cigar. Perhaps he had found a pheasant's nest beside the tracks. Once he found a woman's purse that must have fallen from a train window. It was badly scarred and the handle was broken, but it gave Betsy her first handkerchief, a little pad with a gold pencil and a small bottle of perfume. She kept the purse in her top bureau drawer for years.

That night at dinner, over the fried pork and boiled turnips, Annie Bigley told her husband about Betsy's adventure. Betsy herself had refrained from mentioning it, for after a couple of embarrassing experiences she had learned to avoid telling the same tale twice. The temptation to improve on a story was so strong that she had to watch lest she trap herself.

Besides, it was much more fun to hear someone else telling it as they thought they had heard it from you. They always got something a little wrong—or emphasized something that you hadn't thought was important. Or, they introduced some new and unexpected aspect. Tonight, for instance, she noted that her mother concluded with, "And to think, Dan, that all this wouldn't have happened if the darlings hadn't been out looking for flowers for me just because tomorrow is my birthday!"

Dan, who loved flowers in the field but tended to equate their presence in the home with weddings and funerals, nonetheless got the point. He didn't want it but he got it. And Betsy smiled to herself behind her modestly downcast eyes. Her mother had done it again: turned an almost wholly unrelated event to her own advantage.

Tomorrow was her birthday! Even with her then limited knowledge of biology, Betsy knew that most people had only one birthday a year. Annie sometimes had two or three—well enough spaced so that Dan didn't seem to remember and all of them conveniently timed to match railway pay days.

There didn't seem to be anything especially bad in this. Birthdays were fun. And in the Bigleys' world of limited pleasures and endless work, you had to make your own fun, as Betsy well knew.

She was constantly engaged in doing so. At home, at

school, wherever she went, the need to alleviate boredom, to give life a larger dimension, seemed to be ever present.

Even in her early relationship to boys she was not content to go the route of other girls, giggling together in the school-yard at someone's accidentally undone fly, or suffering early explorations from rough and unsure hands. When a boy came near Betsy, he felt he was approaching a princess. She would draw herself up and gaze at him in such a cold and distant manner that the lad was left stumbling in his speech·or in-articulate.

The teacher in their one-room schoolhouse was quick to notice this. Not knowing that its background lay in play (that Betsy was *being* a princess), she saw in her a rare recog-nition of how all men should be treated, for it had long been her own practice to spurn their advances. The fact that her gray-mouse appearance had induced few such overtures was interpreted by her as proof that firmness worked. They would leave you alone if you let them know their place.

She was constantly dismayed by the free and easy attitude of her farm-bred pupils toward sex. From the age of eight on they were busy experimenting, happily poking and feeling and rolling in the grass. It was shocking. And, occasionally, it was alarming. She always had to keep an eye on the out-house door because that four-holer the local citizens had so generously built with their own hands was, she knew, a Mecca for her experimental biologists.

On several occasions, she had had to interrupt the desk work she did during recess or lunch to go out, drive away the children waiting in line at the knot-holes and pound at the door until it was opened by one of the flush-faced children within.

Betsy—or Elizabeth, as Miss Cushing preferred to call her

—was never involved. She was never in one of the lines waiting to peek. And she was certainly never inside.

More and more, Cassie Cushing found herself turning to Elizabeth as someone with whom she could communicate. She knew full well the dangers in showing favoritism. But the girl never seemed to take advantage of her—and the other children did not seem to mind. Elizabeth became the one who remained behind at recess to wipe the blackboard clean, or lingered at the end of the school day to bang the chalk out of the felt brushes.

At lunch, when all the children from the outlying farms went outdoors to eat (weather permitting), Elizabeth stayed at her desk. And as she and Miss Cushing each delicately picked at the contents of their paper bags, they talked. Not of schoolwork, but of the world.

Miss Cushing was a city girl. She had been born in London. Admittedly, it was London, Ontario, not London, England. But it was a city, with city ways and the city intensifications of human problems.

Even in so simple a social structure as existed in the little village of Eastwood and its rural environs there were clearly recognizable divisions. Without tags applied, there were good people and bad people, rich (relative to the norm) and poor. But in London the good and the bad were multiplied and intensified, the rich were richer and, if only by contrast, the poor seemed poorer.

Miss Cushing thought a lot about this as she went to and from the minister's house where her monthly contribution as a boarder was a welcome addition to the meagre income. She was glad to be out of London, glad to have found a little world where she was recognized as a special person.

Not that she was the kind that sought attention. Far from it. Her whole life style was geared to anonymity. Unlike the famous relative about whom her mother talked constantly, Sir Samuel Cunard, she shunned the attention of others. While his fame grew and grew—so that the humble boy from Nova Scotia now seemed, with his steamboats dominating the Atlantic, quite superhuman—she shrank more and more within herself. This reversal of their trends was not wholly of her choosing, of course. One had to recognize, she could see from the objective distance of Eastwood, that her mother had had a hand in it.

As Cassie grew up, her mother, bored with the unimaginative man she had married, became more and more aware of the difference between her own lower-middle-class life as the wife of a clerk and the glamorous, wealth-eased life of the famous man who bore her parents' name. The fact that Mr. Cushing and she had managed to produce only one child, and that a girl, began to eat at her. Given a son, she could have raised him in her hero's image and perhaps, by somehow getting Sir Samuel to take him into the business, she could have become a part of that wonderful and exciting intercontinental life.

Unfortunately for her daughter, Mrs. Cushing did not keep all these things in her heart. She brought them out quite openly around the family table, or when her daughter displeased her, or in later years, simply when she could get anyone to listen.

On completing secondary school and Normal School, where she was taught to teach, Cassie Cushing packed her bags and set sail, casting off deliberately from the place of her birth. So far, her voyage had taken her only some forty miles, but for now that was enough. Only in her mind in the quiet of the night could she still hear her mother's voice or see her father's whipped-pup eyes.

Perhaps a more experienced teacher would have hesitated

to make one pupil so much her confidante. In the single classroom school where all grades were mixed, there was a real danger in singling out one child, especially a young one. What saved Cassie (and saved Betsy, too, for favorites often suffer in not-so-subtle ways) was that Betsy had already set herself apart.

Alice, Mary, or Emily Bigley—or the four Bigley boys who came and went so unobtrusively and erratically that Cassie was never quite sure which was which and frequently got their assignments confused—none of them was really distinguishable from the general mold of pupils in the school. Betsy alone stood out, attractive, alert, and with a light in her eyes that spoke of some inner fire.

She did not even look like the other Bigley offspring. They all had hair of a reddish hue and tended to be tall and thin like their mother. Betsy was rather short for her age and even at eight her figure was developing a fullness that suggested early maturity. Long brown hair framed a face whose complexion was so fair that it brought to mind the freshness on the cheeks of Scottish immigrant lasses newly arrived from the Highlands.

Betsy's own brothers and sisters saw her as different from themselves, Cassie noted. If they went out of the door as a group, they instinctively paused to let her lead. If she spoke to them (which was seldom in front of others), they all fell silent and listened.

Cassie saw that she was a leader—a leader in an environment that did not tend to develop leadership, for the penalties of the playground were great for those (other than Betsy) who did not choose to run with the pack. Yet she was a leader without a following. Of her own choice she did not exercise her leadership abilities in the school society. It was as if she were saving herself for some more worthy time and place.

This theory was rather sorely tested a few years later, but by then Cassie was so emotionally intermeshed with Betsy that the events were easily rationalized.

In the meantime, it was Cassie who had to have the first disturbing experience. For a long time, she had regaled Elizabeth with stories of the Cunards. While she had rejected her mother for rejecting her, Cassie did see the magic in being part of a family whose name was known across the seven seas. She read every newspaper story, every article she could find, about Sir Samuel, her supposed relative. She found in Elizabeth a rapt, believing audience as she described how he had been knighted, and told of his wealth and the grand way in which he lived.

And then he died. There was no more Sir Samuel Cunard. "Sir Samuel is" became "Sir Samuel was"—a much weaker statement, arrived at through a period of sorrow and re-learning.

Word of his death first reached Cassie throught the minister. He had seen a newspaper, probably the London *Advocate*, in which Sir Samuel was given his last headline. The news was brought back to the manse and broken gently. The minister and his wife, long aware of Cassie's relationship, assumed a family closeness typical of families as they knew them. They were unaware that Cunard had never, to Cassie's knowledge, communicated with any of his Ontario relatives, let alone Cassie's mother. He may never have been aware that Cassie even existed. And yet, in a special way they could not see, their gentleness was justified; for unmet, unknown, and uncaring, Sir Samuel had been so large a part of Cassie's life that his passing was like a subtraction of some vital part of her.

The day that she was told, Cassie perceived her pupils vaguely. The teaching went on by rote, an automatic process conducted by the forefront of the mind. If the others did not sense her remoteness, it was not lost on Betsy. She saw that something was wrong, that Miss Cushing was not really there in front of them.

At the end of the day, when the others had gone, Betsy came up the aisle quietly and put her hand on the shoulder of the drab little figure at the rough pine desk.

"What's wrong?"

Cassie looked up and said, "He's gone. Sir Samuel. Dead."

Betsy knelt beside her and rested her chin on Cassie's leg like a dog. "I'm sorry."

Cassie stroked her hair. "And I never met him. I was going to someday, you know. Someday." She stood up and Betsy scrambled to her feet. "Walk home with me?"

They went down the village street saying nothing. When they got to the minister's house Cassie said, "Would you come—would you like to come in?" And Betsy nodded.

There was no one home. Cassie led the way up to her simple room at the back of the second floor. A bureau, a corner curtained off as a clothes cupboard, a bed with a high oak back carved in flowers, a chair with a rush seat, a washstand with the pitcher sitting in the bowl and one brush in the matching toothbrush mug, some books piled in a corner for lack of a better place. And that was all. Betsy looked around and stood uncertainly.

"I can't believe it!" Cassie said, sitting down on the side of the bed. She held out her hand and Betsy went to sit beside her. "He wasn't that old. Why did he have to die?"

"We had a cat once that died. Papa said it was just because he was tired of living."

Cassie put her arm around her. "But this man wasn't like that! He couldn't be tired of living. He was living like a king. He *was* a king, you know. A king among men. I can't believe

12

it. All day long I've been saying that. It just can't be true! My head keeps going round and round and all I can think to say is 'I can't believe it!' "

"Why don't you rest a while?" Betsy suggested. "Maybe —could I read to you a little?"

Cassie nodded dumbly. "Yes," she said in a moment, "Yes, that would be nice. You read very well."

She stretched out on the Bed. Betsy picked up one of the books in the corner, came back and curled up beside her.

It was, she found, a history book and a dull one at that, for it dwelt only on facts and had no people saying things in it. She was not, therefore, greatly surprised to find before long that her audience had fallen asleep. She pulled up the comforter from the foot of the bed to cover the slight form and quietly tiptoed from the room and down the stairs. She walked home through the dark end of the day, thinking about death and greatness and the greatness of death.

And then the hot weather was on them with a rush. The smell of damp clothing in the class became the acrid, armpit smell of summer. Even more than her pupils, Cassie Cushing longed to be out of doors. It was required that the lessons continue to the end of June. (But not a day longer, for the boys and girls were needed on the farms.)

It seemed impossible for each day to be longer than the last—and yet it was. And when the wind was still and the sun beat down, the school became an oven that baked out thought and burned ambition and left a crust of wasted time.

Saturdays and Sundays, all too few and all the more welcome, were the weekly days of freedom. Cassie asked Elizabeth if she would like to go on a picnic.

In the kitchen of the manse Cassie made up sandwiches. And in a preserve jar sealed tight with its red rubber ring she put some cool well water. Elizabeth came running down the street and they went walking in the fine, free Saturday morning air.

"Sir Samuel is" had now become "Sir Samuel was" indeed, but still the stories flowed, and perhaps even improved in the telling, as Sir Samuel's death freed Cassie's dreams from the constraints of reality.

They came to the stream and walked along its bank.

"It's here the boys go swimming," laughed Elizabeth. "I've watched. Through those big bushes over there."

"Suppose they'd seen you!" Cassie protested.

"Oh, they're worse than girls! They'd just all yell and jump in the water until I went away. Why are people like that, Miss Cushing? Why are we all ashamed of ourselves, of being seen like we really are?"

"*As* we really are? I don't know, Elizabeth. It's just human nature, I suppose."

The bank was steeper now. Elizabeth grabbed the branch of an overhanging tree and swung herself down to the water's edge. Cassie followed her with difficulty.

"This is my place," the girl explained. "See, you can sit here on these stones and nobody knows you're down here."

It was true. The willows hung low over the water, forming a cool, green cave with a liquid floor.

"This is where I swim. Do you want to?" Elizabeth began taking off her clothes. Cassie hesitated. "Are you sure no one will see us?" The girl grinned. "They haven't yet!" Before Cassie had undone her petticoat, Elizabeth was in the water, a little white dolphin at play.

They sat on the stones to dry before dressing.

"But why is it human nature?" asked Elizabeth, picking up the earlier topic. "I mean, all the other animals take it for granted. They don't have clothes. They don't giggle."

Cassie knew there was an answer; somewhere in the Old Testament, she thought.

"Of course," Elizabeth went on, "boys do look silly. I mean," she said shyly, testing the conversation's acceptability, "they have those—those funny things down front." She looked at her teacher. "You know, and sometimes the things stick straight out or up just like the ones on bulls. Why do they do that, Miss Cushing?"

"Well," said Cassie, feeling her way in turn, "I guess it's for the same reason. The boys are becoming men."

"And men are like bulls?"

"That's it."

"Then we are like cows?"

"To men we are."

"So then," said Elizabeth, sliding over closer to her teacher, "where cows have udders we have these?" She pointed to Cassie's nearest breast. Cassie nodded. "Will I have breasts like you someday?"

"I expect so. Most women do. Yours will be growing soon." Cassie laid a gentle hand on the girl's chest.

"Oh, I hope so!" Elizabeth laughed. "I think we're so much prettier than boys." She put her hand, in turn, on Cassie's breast. "It's so round and soft."

Cassie had always been ashamed of her smallness. It was the first time anyone outside of her parents or doctor had touched her there. It was a good feeling. Putting her arm around Elizabeth's little shoulders she leaned back against the bank, drawing the girl with her. "This is nice."

Betsy lay beside her and, exploring, slid her hand down from the mounds above to the mound below. "What a strange thing!" she whispered, running her fingers through the light brown hair. "Your hair. I mean the hair on your head is all straight and this is all curly. Will mine be curly too?"

Cassie smiled into her eyes. "I'm sure it will. But that's a few years off." She stroked the bare little bump before her. "You're still all smooth and new."

"Still," Betsy sighed, "it might be nice to have one of those things the boys have. I feel there's—there's something missing. You know?"

"Oh, but you do have one!" exclaimed her teacher. "Only ours are nicely hidden. Didn't you know? Here," she rolled a bit on her side, "give me your hand." She took a finger gently and guided it. "Do you feel that? That's mine. It's very small—and nobody ever sees it. But it's there."

Betsy tried futilely to find her own. "Does it get big and hard like theirs?"

"Yes, but all within its limits. If you are nice to it, it really grows and feels good."

The teacher ran her fingers through the girl's hair and settled back against the bank.

"You have to be very gentle," she said. "Gentle. Gentle."

They walked back to the village in happy silence. Cassie knew that she and Elizabeth were now as close as friends could be, and she was glad that now she had someone who could share the exciting, secret feelings which long ago she had discovered for herself. Betsy was full of wonder at it all, fascinated by the ability of one person to give such pleasure to another—and, at the same time, not unaware of the power it gave you over that other person, for she had seen the true nakedness of love, the defencelessness of a person caught up in the building to the bursting of the dam.

During the next few years their friendship continued and developed. Before long, any pretense of education in sex was abandoned and it became an automatic thing for them to undress and lie together whenever they were alone. Their play progressed from manual to oral stimulation quite naturally as Betsy began to awaken to womanhood.

Far from the world of sexual sophisticates, by simple experiment they discovered *soixante-neuf* and often spent long, slow, happy hours like that, making the excitement last.

Then came the change. Betsy began to menstruate. With this evidence of growing up, she became restless. She found herself less eager to climb the stairs to Cassie's room. The long hours on the bed became long hours indeed.

Besides, Cassie's conversation was getting boring. A long time ago, Betsy had withdrawn from her mother when she discovered that all her stories about Santa Claus had been lies. (She did not blame her father for his part in those lies. It was her mother who told them. He just nodded.) Now she suspected that while Sir Samuel Cunard might, indeed, have had some family connection with the Cushings, it was a lot slighter than Cassie wanted to believe. In fact, Betsy doubted if the teacher really knew anything more about him than the press had provided. For a while, Betsy played a little game in which she would get Cassie to repeat one of her anecdotes about him and then count the number of places in which it had changed since the last time. However, even this became a dull exercise in learning to be consistent in one's lies, and Betsy began to look around her, seeking a new challenge.

The proof of her womanhood excited her. She still did not see anything attractive in boys of her own age. They all seemed stupid and rough. Yet the urge was there, developed early with Cassie but not fully satisfied.

She began to dress a little more carefully, to experiment with ways of doing her hair. If the family had any errand at the village store, she was always quick to volunteer. It was in this way that she met Tom Wolsey.

Chronologically, Tom was thirty-two that year. Emotionally, he was probably seventeen. Mentally, he hovered around eight or nine. His wife had died the year before and the nights were becoming increasingly long and lonely out on the farm which he had fortunately inherited from his parents. Local custom had it that he could not marry for at least another year. But his glands knew nothing of customs.

Walking back from the village one evening, he caught up with Betsy. She was carrying a sack of sugar and he took it from her and slung it easily over his shoulder. They walked along, making idle talk, with Tom growing increasingly conscious that he was with a female.

He didn't know much about her. Dan Bigley's oldest daughter. Still went to school, which was kind of impressive; Tom had been frightened badly by numbers at an early age. She kept pretty much to herself, he'd heard. Well, so did he. In the dusk he paused and pointed. "Want to take a short cut?" Betsy looked at him with her wise eyes. "All right."

There was a zig-zag split-rail fence. He climbed over it, put down the sugar and lifted her down from the top rail. She came against his chest and he could feel the soft pressure of her young breasts. It was such a wonderful feeling, after a whole year, that for a long moment he did not move. And then he kissed her. Not hard. Not hard at first. But then the hunger in him surged and his arms were wrapped around her and her head was back with his mouth pressing down on hers and his manhood stirred.

For a moment he had a flutter of fear. Suppose she panicked and ran—ran screaming to her father? But then he felt it. He felt her little hand creep in between them and cup him. He drew back and laid her gently on the hay. Throwing himself down beside her he began to wrestle frantically with the brass buttons of his fly.

"Here, wait," she whispered. Sitting up, she pressed him down upon his back and carefully and slowly undid the buttons for him. Tom tried to sit up but she would have

18

none of it. Instead, she stroked him lightly and lovingly. "Oh God!" he groaned, "you've got to let me do it."

"Not tonight," she said, "but soon." She smiled and, bending down, gave him a gentle kiss. Then, before Tom had collected his wits, she was up and gone, sugar sack and all, over the fence and running down the road toward the lights of home.

She was thirteen, he found out. And while there were stories—some true, some wish-fulfillment—about almost every other girl for miles around, there were no stories about Betsy. She was the teacher's pet and was so good in school that now the teacher was even coaching her at night. They said she might go away to college. Since no one from the village or the area had ever done that, even the prospect of it set her apart. But only thirteen.

Tom thought a lot about Betsy in his slow way. Mostly he thought about the scene in the hayfield. And the more he thought about it, the more committed he became to picking up where they had left off.

He caught up with her again a few nights later. It was a warm, still night with just a slice of moon. "Why wouldn't you the other night?" he asked as they walked along the dirt road.

"I don't know how," she answered quietly. No protest, no rejection, just the simple woman-logic reply.

He stopped her and put his arm around her. "I'll show you."

She turned to face him and, as he looked down at the little face in its brown hair frame his hands went out to cup her breasts.

"Will it hurt?"

"A little bit at first, maybe. But I'll be gentle. You'll like it."

Unabashedly she put her hand on his crotch. "But you're

so big!" He pulled her to him and the blood pounded into his loins and he was hard and ready.

"See?" she said, "It has gotten big again!" She stroked him through the rough cloth of his overalls. His hands were clutching her little buttocks, pressing her against him. "Betsy," he groaned, "please, Betsy!"

"I'm afraid," she whispered.

"Why? It will be all right!"

Betsy pushed herself free.

"My brother Bill told me he heard about a man and a girl that were—you know—doing it. The man was very big and got stuck. He couldn't get it out. He got so frantic he had a heart attack and died and there the poor girl was with that dead man on her."

"What did she do?" asked Tom, peering at her in the dark.

"Oh, she died too," said Betsy. "Went out of her mind and died. They never did get them apart and had to bury them together."

"Well," said Tom, "that won't happen to us, I promise you. I'll go slow, you'll see."

"But Tom, if I do it people will know. I'll have to leave home—and I can't because I'm saving every cent to pay for college!"

"Don't worry about that," he whispered in her hair, "I've got money. I'll give you money. I'll give you ten dollars!"

She kissed him reflectively. "College takes a lot of money."

"I have my farm," he said eagerly, "I can borrow money on that. I'll—I'll give you fifty! Come on, let's climb the fence again! I'll borrow the money tomorrow and bring it to you after school."

Betsy looked up and down the road. No one was in sight and the night was still.

"Let me see it again," she whispered. Tom reached down

and brought it out. "Are you sure?" she worried. "It seems so big and I'm so small. See!" She lifted the long skirts she was wearing. There was nothing underneath. Nothing except the little mound of hair between the white pillars of her thighs. Tom put his hand on it and she smiled up at him.

"You bring the money and meet me here tomorrow night at nine." She dropped her skirts and, with a final touching of him, turned and ran.

The next day was a long one for poor Tom Wolsey. But by nine that night he had his fifty dollar loan on the home he had inherited and was fighting a wildcat in the hayfield. Betsy's fear of his size seemed to fade once the money was in her hands. And if she was ignorant of the ways of men in heat, she made up for it in apparent enthusiasm for the results.

She missed school the next morning but showed up at noon, all excited, waving a letter.

"Look, Miss Cushing!" she cried, "I just got a letter from a lawyer! An uncle of mine I didn't even know has died and left me a fortune!"

"How wonderful!" Cassie cried, reaching for the letter, "Let me see!"

"Here, I'll read it to you," said Betsy. "Dear Miss Bigley, We regret to inform you of the passage of your late uncle, Simon Bolivar. In his will he left you fifteen thousand dollars the which we will be forwarding to you shortly. Regretfully yours, Adam Smith, Lawyer."

"Fifteen thousand dollars! Why, think Elizabeth, that's —that's more than enough to buy a farm in these parts!"

"Yes, I know," said Elizabeth.

"What are you going to do with it all? I hope you'll put it in the bank and save it for when you go to college. You are certainly very fortunate. Just think, an heiress at thirteen!"

Betsy looked at her and smiled. Then, turning slowly, she went out into the hubbub of the noon-hour play, walked through the yard and down the road, and never came back.

The morning train took her to the town of Woodstock, the next stop on the line to London. Heeding her teacher's advice, she went directly to the community's one bank. Betsy had never been inside a bank before but from her reading she knew what to expect.

This particular bank was an exceptionally dull and dusty example. Even the three people working in it seemed dull and dusty. She thought how little fun it must be to be shut up all day behind those brass bars. Of course, one could always play with the money!

The young but sallow man behind the little glass window in the bars looked down his nose at her as she approached. He was ambitious and had already learned the first rule of banking: always make the customer feel uncomfortable and a little guilty.

"Are you the manager?" Betsy asked primly.

"What can I do for you?" he rejoined haughtily, evading her question.

"I would like to give you some money to keep for me," Betsy replied, imitating his tone. "This letter will explain." She pushed the letter she had shown Cassie through the gap under the glass.

The teller read it through and began to wish he had called the manager. Then he read it again. Getting credit for bringing in a big account wouldn't do him any harm.

"Congratulations, Miss Bigley!" he said, his voice warming. "How much do you want to deposit?"

"I want to put in thirty dollars," said Betsy. When she saw his smile begin to fade she added, "To start."

"Well," he said, "That's a beginning, isn't it?" His smile

was so thin Betsy wondered if he had any teeth. "The first step is to open an account. Would you be good enough to fill out this card and sign it?"

The necessary steps having been taken, the teller gave her a nice little book in which he had written the amount of her deposit. And then he handed her a pad of small, elongated sheets of green paper. Each sheet had the name of the bank printed on it in beautifully-shaped big black letters.

"What's this for?" asked Betsy, flicking through it.

He smiled his slice of smile again. "That's so you can buy things. Those are checks. When you want to pay for something at a store, you just write the name of the store or whatever up there, then the amount you want to spend below on that next line, add the date and your account number and sign it. Then it's just like cash."

"That's wonderful!" Betsy exclaimed. "I wish we had a bank in Eastwood!"

"When you need more checks, just let us know," the teller assured her genially. "We've got lots."

Betsy wandered out bemused, waving the pad like a magic wand. So that was how all those people in the parlor cars of the trains got rich; they just wrote checks!

Across the street from the bank she saw a jewellery store. She went over and looked in the window. The proprietor had seen her emerge from the bank and approach. He beckoned to her to come in.

"Can I help you?"

Betsy walked along slowly, peering into the curved glass tops of the display counters. "I would like—" she paused, her wand in her hand, "I would like—a gold bracelet."

"Yes, indeed, Miss!" the jeweller responded, eyeing the pad of checks. "I think we have just the thing!" He selected a thick and ornately carved arm ring that he had been trying

23

to unload for years. Removing the price tag, he slipped the ornament over her small, white hand. "There! Isn't that a beauty? And it's solid gold plate, too! On you it looks great!"

Betsy nodded. The bracelet was so shiny it almost sparkled. A few minutes later, with the help of his pen, she had sold her first piece of fiction; the price he had quoted her exceeded her deposit in the bank. Had he charged her what was written on the price tag that lay crumpled in his pocket, she would still have had a balance of fifteen dollars.

There was a clothing store next door. A real emporium with dresses and gloves and hats and all sorts of wonderful things. Betsy went in and played happily for almost half an hour, going from department to department, looking, feeling, posing in front of the full-length swivel mirrors. Finally, she came back to the dress section and bought two for herself and a skirt for Alice. Alice was having to do her chores for her. The clerk tried to suggest tactfully that the dresses were really for an older person. Betsy was annoyed. It was really too bad that they didn't have women working in the store. Men just didn't understand. She was even more annoyed when she saw him lift an eyebrow when she produced her pad of checks. She said, a little defensively, "The manager at the bank just gave them to me."

The clerk wanted to ask "But are they good?" However, her sweet earnestness, forthright manner, and the huge, swaying bracelet influenced his judgment. The necessary pen was produced, dipped in the ink well on the wrapping counter, and Betsy happily wrote her second piece of sold fiction.

She hadn't really liked that clerk she decided as she went down the street, her bundles under her arm. That raised eyebrow had bothered her. Just because she was from Eastwood didn't give Woodstock folks any right to put on airs!

Her eye was caught by a window display which exhibited various examples of printing in rather faded and dusty condition. Invitations to weddings, notices of farm auctions, announcements of the coming of long-gone travelling shows and, below them all, an array of business cards. She had never seen cards like that before. Peering through the grimy window she read as many of them as she could. And then an idea came to her.

"Can you print something for me while I wait?" she asked the gnome at the roll-top desk inside.

"If it isn't too long," he admitted grudgingly, putting his jam jar of rye whiskey back in its drawer.

"I want some little cards like those in the window."

"Business cards?" He smiled and dried the smile with the back of his hand. "What kind of business would you be in?"

Betsy shook her head. "No business. I just want cards to give people so they'll know who I am."

After watching him set type letter by letter to her instructions and turn the crank on his creaking press, Betsy received her little supply of cards, and the printer got in exchange one of her magic pieces of paper.

"Nice printing job," he commented, holding the check up to the light. "Wish I had a press could do that. Be careful of those cards; they take a while to dry."

The afternoon was drawing to a close. The long day had been made the more tiring because of the ride on the train. It took it out of you, hiding in the tiny lavatory to avoid the conductor with his ticket punch. It was boring too, even though it was fun now and then to step on the flush pedal and look down the toilet to see the track ties flying by below. The sign on the wall said "Passengers Will Please Refrain From Flushing When the Train Is in the Station," but out in the country—as her father well knew—the passengers flushed

25

at will. "One of the hazards of the job," he called it.

The evening train back would be leaving soon. Betsy, clutching her pad of checks tightly, wished that she didn't have to take it.

Presto! She looked up and there she was, outside a hotel! It said right over the door "Accommodation for Men and Horses." Assuming that women were not excluded, she marched up the porch steps and went in.

To the man behind the counter she said "I would like to have a bed."

He looked at her a little coldly. In the half-dark of the lobby he couldn't decide. If she was one of *those* women, she sure was a small one!

"You mean you want a room?"

"Yes, please. For the night."

"Are you from out of town?"

"Yes," said Betsy, passing him one of her barely-dry cards, "I am."

The manager held her card close to his eyes and read aloud. "Miss Elizabeth Bigley." There was some smaller type underneath the name. He squinted. "Heiress to a Fortune."

Well, he thought, at least she's not a woman of the streets! He had never seen a card quite like that before. It didn't make much sense, but there it was. He had a great respect for things in print, having been raised on the Bible.

"Do you have any baggage?" he inquired as he took down a key from the small hook-board behind him.

"No," said Betsy, "I didn't plan to stay when I left home. I just came over to put some money in the bank, but then I went shopping."

The next morning, Betsy was up at her usual go-to-school time. As she was hungry, she dressed and went out to find a restaurant. What with trying new things to eat and window-shopping on the way back, it was well after ten when she returned to the hotel. To her surprise, she found her new dresses and the skirt for Alice piled on a chair in the lobby. Beside them stood a large, ferocious-looking man in a bulging blue uniform.

"Be you Elizabeth Bigley?" he demanded as she approached.

Betsy nodded.

He looked at her sharply. Her obvious youth was unexpected. "Well then, best you come with me," he ordered, scooping up her purchases. "These all the things you bought?"

Hooking his free hand under her arm, he marched her out through the door.

"How old are you?" he asked as he guided her down the street.

"Thirteen," she replied, adding a "Sir" instinctively.

"Ever been arrested before?"

Betsy shook her head, feeling very miserable. Arrested! "What's wrong?" she asked. "What did I do?"

"Oh come now, lass!" he protested as he turned her toward the entrance of the town jail. "If you be smart enough to do it, you be smart enough to know what you did."

He ushered her down a long hall to the cells and put her in one.

"You've had breakfast? Good. Well then, Sam will be around with lunch afore long. Be nice to him and he might even give you something fit to eat."

"How long must I stay here?" Betsy asked through the bars, frightened by what was happening to her, repelled by the dank, badly-lit place.

"Until the magistrate shows up. He's been and gone for today. Tomorrow morning, likely." He turned to leave and

27

paused. "I'm sorry, lass, but there's naught that I can do."

Betsy sank down on the hard cot that was fastened to one wall. There wasn't anyone else in the cells. Silence. For a moment she thought that she was going to cry but then she reached into the pocket of her skirt and brought out one of her cards. Heiress to a fortune.

It would be all right. Her father's lawyers would arrive soon. Perhaps her father would come himself in his big, black silk tophat and flowing cape, carrying his shiny walking-stick with the big diamond on top.

The policeman would usher him in, abject in his apologies for the terrible mistake they had made. "If only we had realized who she was!" he would keep repeating.

Betsy got so excited at the picture of rescue and retribution that she began to walk up and down, gesturing excitedly as the conversation continued in her mind. When the scene ended it was re-played, examined, played again.

Noon came. Sam turned out to be a turnkey with a limp. He clanged his ring of keys along the bars as he came.

"Hungry?" he asked, peering in.

"Very," said Betsy truthfully.

"I'll get you something from the restaurant around the corner. Pork or fish?"

"I would rather fancy the fish," said the heiress and then, breaking down, "But first I've got to go."

"Eh? Oh, well, come on. It's at the end of the hall." He found the right key and opened her door. "Go ahead. But I have to go with you. Regulations."

Betsy glanced at the hot little eyes in his fat face and decided that he made his own regulations when it suited him. However, she had no choice. He followed her into the small toilet and watched with interest as she performed.

"Better?"

"Oh yes!" she acknowledged as she re-arranged her clothing. Her concern really was not so much to preserve modesty as somehow to get everything back in place without dropping the last of Tom's money and her little supply of cards. In consequence, the turnkey was treated to an apparently satisfying glimpse of her little white bottom. He was grinning a wet grin as he led her back. For a moment she thought he was going to follow her into the cell but he apparently lost his nerve. He closed the door and limped off.

After the lunch of greasy, cold fish had been eaten, Betsy stretched out on the cot and slept for a while. It was a mistake, for when the supper hour had come and gone—another glimpse for Sam, another plate of bad food—she was wide awake and terribly aware of her aloneness.

It seemed that the long black night would never end. And yet it did. There *was* a tomorrow. There was a breakfast, preceded by a trip with Sam, who this time got so close that she thought he was going to eat what he saw, and then the policeman came back.

"Are you all right, lass?" he asked. His eyes flicked toward Sam as he spoke.

"Oh yes, officer, thank you! Can I go now?"

"To court you can." He motioned to Sam to unlock the door. "His Honor is waiting."

They went out of the cell block and into a large square room with gray walls. It had the kind of molded sheet-metal ceiling that reminded her of the Loyal Orange Lodge in Eastwood where her father went as a Mason to perform the secret rites and decry the growing number of Catholics.

Along one side of the room was a sort of high counter. There was a Union Jack on a pole behind it and a framed picture of Queen Victoria. Below the picture, a gray and wrinkled man sat writing in a big book.

"Is this the girl?" he asked without looking up.

"It is, indeed, Your Honor."

"Get the others in here."

The policeman motioned for Betsy to sit on a bench along the opposite wall. "Wait here," he ordered and went out again.

In a few minutes he was back, followed by the jeweller, the clerk from the dress shop, the printer, and the man from the hotel. Betsy smiled at each of them but they did not smile back.

The magistrate put down the pen with the long white feather and glowered at the group.

"Now what's all this?" he grumped.

The policeman stepped forward. "These men claim that this lass here, Elizabeth Bigley, bought from them and gave them worthless checks."

"All of you?"

"Not me," said the hotel man. "I ain't been paid at all yet."

"There was some money, Your Honor," said the jeweller. "When I got to the bank this morning, they told me that. But not enough for my check and they wouldn't give me what there was. Then the rest come in for theirs and the bank manager wouldn't give any to any of us. Says he's sitting tight until he's sure which got a check from her first. I say it was me. I seen her come out of the bank and she came straight over to my place."

Betsy slid the bracelet up under her sleeve.

The judge's sharp eyes focussed on her. "All right, young lady, what do you have to say?"

Betsy stood up. "I just did what the bank man told me," she protested. "I went to put some money in because I didn't want to lose it and he gave me a little pad of paper. He said anytime I wanted anything all I had to do was write on one of the sheets and that made it like money. I gave each of these men, except the hotel man, one of the sheets and they seemed to think it was fine when I did it. I was going to give the hotel man one too, but the policeman took me away and put me in jail before I could."

"How old are you?"

"Thirteen."

"You look older."

"I know," said Betsy. "That's what everyone says."

The magistrate had been given one of her cards. He held it up. "And what's all this about?"

"Well," said Betsy, "I'm a stranger here. I thought it would help if people knew who I was."

"Heiress to a fortune, eh? In that case, I suppose you'll have no trouble making good on these checks! You do understand that you can't write checks unless you have enough money in the bank for each of them?"

Betsy thought quickly. "I can't pay right way," she said, stalling. She looked down. Her thick-soled black shoes that yesterday were scuffed and worn were now new-looking and they had big gold buckles on them. "You see, my rich uncle has just died. I haven't got the money yet. When I get it I will return and repay them an hundredfold."

"An hundredfold, eh? Sounds like Bible talk. You a Baptist?"

"On my mother's side," Betsy hedged. "My father is Anglican."

"What's he do?"

"He's employed by the railroad."

The constable cleared his throat. "I've been checking, your Honor. He works the track out of Eastwood and farms a bit. Large family, little food. Good people. This, they say, is the odd one."

31

The magistrate stared at her and nodded. "Odd one is right! Anyone who goes around doing what she has been doing at thirteen is more than odd. I'd say she's crazy."

He sighed and turned to the plaintiffs. "Well now, let's see. The dresses are back and no worse for it, I gather. What about the jewellery?"

Betsy reluctantly took off her bracelet and held it out. The jeweller came over and took it from her.

"There's not much we can do about the printing or the hotel room, I guess. I'll go by the bank and tell Arnold to split what there is between you and that'll have to be it." He pivoted back to Betsy and pointed a finger at her. "As for you, young lady, I am going to assume that you are not in possession of all your faculties. If I'm right, I hope you grow out of it. If I'm wrong, God help us all! Now, Constable Higgins here is going to take the rest of the day off from his police work and escort you back to Eastwood.

"Not only that, Mr. Higgins, but you're going to take her straight to her parents and tell them what happened. At her age, after that it's up to them. But if you ever see her in Woodstock again I want you to arrest her on sight."

He glowered around the room. "As for you businessmen, I have a suggestion to make, especially to my friend the jeweller because he bit first. When the day comes that you're so hungry for a dollar that you can't tell the difference between a crazy young girl and a legitimate customer, I think it's time you checked your own sanity. Now, all of you get out of here. Court's dismissed."

That morning, Cassie encountered Tom Wolsey as she was entering school. A fine, handsome man, she thought, not very bright perhaps, but—well—virile. She did no more than bid him good morning. But when she saw him still standing outside the gate as she was leaving school, she felt it proper to stop.

"Hello, Tom. Are you waiting for someone?"

He looked uncomfortable. "No—well, yes, I am, ma'am. I —I'd heard tell that one of the girls—Dan Bigley's daughter, Betsy—might be interested in doing a little housework. I— since my wife died—I sort of need somebody to, you know, kind of tidy up and all. But I haven't seen her."

Cassie shook her head. "Neither have I, Tom. Her sisters tell me she's left home. They don't know where. But it's my guess she's decided to take a little trip." Cassie suppressed a sigh. "Can't say that I blame her, now that she's an heiress."

"A what, ma'am?"

"Oh, didn't you hear? She has come into a lot of money."

"Yes, ma'am, I mean—that's nice ma'am. Do you think she'll come back?" he asked anxiously.

"Oh, I'm sure she will! She's just having a little fling. Probably gone over to a relative's in London for a few days. Tell you what," said Cassie impulsively, "if you're really stuck until she returns, would you like me to come and sort of put things in order? It will tide you over until Elizabeth—Betsy— gets back."

"I couldn't do that!" Tom protested. "You're—well, you're the school teacher!"

"I still know how to run a house. Why don't we go over to your place right now and get started?"

Tom shrugged. "Well, all right, ma'am. If you really mean it."

Cassie started off down the road beside him, wondering what had gotten into her. She only knew that she missed Elizabeth very much. Elizabeth's good fortune and sudden departure had left a void. Much as she hated the thought of having to work for a man, perhaps Elizabeth would appreciate what she was doing for her.

On the following day she had a visitor. The pupils had left and Cassie was about to follow them when the door creaked open and a woman she had never seen before stuck her head in, looked around, saw Cassie at her desk, and entered. She was a tall, thin, nervous type of person. For the visit she had put on her Sunday best. As soon as Cassie saw the reddish hair that supported the flat-topped hat with its brimload of feathers, she knew who it was.

Mrs. Bigley came up to the desk and introduced herself. "I hope I'm not intruding," she said, "but I felt I had to talk with you."

"It's perfectly all right," Cassie assured her, motioning for her to take the chair beside the desk, "I wish more of the parents would come to see me. You have a fine family, Mrs. Bigley."

Mrs. Bigley smiled proudly. "Oh, I guess they'll do. The boys are a little wild. Half the time I don't know where they are. But they all make it home for meals, so it's not them I worry about. It's Betsy, Miss Cushing."

"I know what you mean," said Cassie. "She's different from the rest, isn't she? It's as if she had been born an adult."

Mrs. Bigley nodded. "That's the whole truth. She always was sort of strange. Right from the day we got her she has worried me. Not that being different is bad, you know? She can't help being that, bless her! But—well, I guess part of the problem is me. I always have the feeling that she is so much brighter than I am and I think that somewhere back of those eyes of hers she's laughing at me. It—it makes me uncomfortable."

"Well, she *is* a very intelligent girl, you know. I'm sure she isn't laughing at you, but I know what you mean. Have you heard from her?"

Mrs. Bigley looked down at her hands. "That's why I've come today. I need some advice and I figured that there was no one else that I could talk to—no one who knows Betsy as well, you know?"

"What's happened?"

"She's home. They brought her home from over to Woodstock. A policeman. On the afternoon train. He borrowed a buggy at the livery stable and drove her right out to the house. Gave me an awful lecture. I was glad Dan—that's my husband—wasn't home or there'd have been a real scene. Dan wouldn't have let that constable talk like that to me."

"What did he say?"

"He—he—," Mrs. Bigley gripped her hands together, "he says Betsy's not right in the head and that I should have known that and that I shouldn't have let her wander off. I'm supposed to keep her at home now. She got arrested, Miss Cushing!"

"Oh, the poor girl! What had she done?"

Mrs. Bigley leaned forward. "Do you think she's crazy?"

"Of course not! Far from it! But she does have a very active mind. She's very good at imagining things. Tell me what happened."

"Well, I really don't understand it all. But apparently she got some money somewhere. I don't even know how much. She took the train to Woodstock and went into the bank there. At fourteen!"

"You mean thirteen."

"What? Oh yes, yes that's right. Thirteen. My, here I am coming up to forty and I've never seen inside a bank once!

Anyway, the constable says she showed the bank man a letter that said she had inherited a lot of money. Then she opened an account. Can you imagine?"

"Well," said Cassie, "part of that may be my fault. She read me the letter when it came and we discussed what she was going to do with all that money. She said she was going to save it for college and I know putting it in a bank was mentioned."

"Yes, Miss Cushing, but there is no such money! My husband and I have no brothers with money like that—dead or alive. And if we had, I'm sure they'd leave it all to their children, not just one of ours!"

"But I saw the letter!"

Mrs. Bigley looked ashamed. "I think she wrote it herself."

Cassie found herself rising to Betsy's defence. "But you just agreed that she has lots of imagination. There's nothing wrong in a girl pretending. And opening a bank account is a good thing for her to have done. Of course, she shouldn't have lied to the bank."

"But that's not all!" Mrs. Bigley said miserably. "Then she went out and found a printer and had some little cards printed. You know, like society ladies have. The constable gave me one. It says, 'Miss Elizabeth Bigley, Heiress to a Fortune'!"

"It says what?"

"'Miss Elizabeth Bigley' in big letters. Underneath, in smaller letters, it says 'Heiress to a Fortune'! Then," Mrs. Bigley plunged on, "she went to the big hotel there, showed her card to the man at the desk and asked for a room. I gather the man thought she was just playing, being so young and all. Anyway, she got the room and she bought some things in stores. Everywhere she went, she paid by writing checks on the bank. Only, the checks weren't any good because she had only put in about thirty dollars to start with—and Lord only knows where she got that!"

"How did they find out?"

"I'm not exactly sure. I think it was when the storekeepers went to the bank to get their money. As soon as they found how little there was they headed for the police."

"Was she put in jail?"

"All night. Then she was up before some judge. He talked to her for a while and decided—decided she was crazy. So he arranged for her to be brought home and, like the constable said, 'be put into my custody.' What am I going to do, Miss Cushing? Should I strap her?"

Cassie got up and went to the window. Poor Elizabeth! The little bird trapped in the farmhouse cage. After a moment, "She has been punished, Mrs. Bigley. Try to imagine how she felt being taken by the police, locked up in jail, and brought back on the train. Even having to go to the livery stable and hear the policeman explain why he needed a buggy. By now the story of her arrest is all over the village. When the children come to school tomorrow they will all know about it. I'm afraid it's going to be hard on her brothers and sisters for a while. But it's going to be especially hard on her."

"Would you see her?"

"Certainly. I'd be glad to. But not here. I think it would be better if she didn't come back to school for a while."

"But what will we do with her? She won't stay home, I know."

Cassie ran a finger along the window ledge. It was dusty.

"Perhaps she should work for a while. Tom Wolsey is looking for someone."

"But she couldn't stay there! He's a widower. It wouldn't be good—you know?"

Cassie sighed within herself and turned to face the mother.

"On the contrary, I think it would be perfectly all right. After all, he's almost old enough to be her father. He's a good man. And, if it will help any, I'll keep an eye on things. Even if I feel that she shouldn't come back to school for a while, I don't want her to get behind in her studies. After all, she's my prize pupil! So, I'll talk to Tom about that. Some days I'll go over to his place. Others, I'll get him to bring her to the manse. One way or the other we'll keep her mind busy. Between her housework and her books I don't think she'll have time to get into trouble."

"Well," said Mrs. Bigley, "I'll talk it over with Dan."

"And get Elizabeth to come to see me. At the manse. I'll take her to see Tom."

The next day Tom Wolsey had an experience with which he found it hard to cope. Looking up from hoeing the vegetable garden in the front yard, he saw Miss Cushing and Betsy walking in from the road. While his heart raced at the sight of the girl, the presence of the school teacher introduced a decidedly confusing element.

He had had no doubt on the day the teacher tidied up for him that with a little persuasion she could be aroused. And, assuming that Betsy was gone forever (and his money with her), he had developed the conviction that maybe the teacher would trade. He didn't really think it through, but the essence of his thought-groping was that a little intellectual stimulation would not do him any harm—and it seemed, from all that he could see, that a little physical stimulation might not hurt her. It could be a very fair exchange.

Given the hours he had to think about his half-formed proposition in the fields, the end result had become virtually a reality in his mind. He had rehearsed so often what he would say and do that not only the opening moves but even the deep plunging and the rearing-back-to-drive-again of her awakening to the joys of sex had been worked over so thoroughly that he felt embarrassed to see her.

Betsy was wearing her best clothes and carrying a bundle. She walked firmly and surely beside Miss Cushing, never taking her eyes off Tom as they drew near.

"Tom," said Miss Cushing, "Elizabeth has come home. I've told her you were looking for help and she would like the job—if it's still open."

"Oh—oh, it's open. Yes—yes, it's open all right. That is, if she—" he turned to Betsy awkwardly, "if you want it."

The girl said nothing. Her shoulders were back and she stared at him coolly.

"She does," said the teacher. "She'll stay here and you'll pay her something. It doesn't have to be much, so long as she gets her victuals. But there's one condition. She's got to go on with her learning. So, you've got to see she studies when the chores are done. I'll come out a couple of times a week to see where she is in her books. And once or twice a week—whenever you're coming in to the store, say—I want you to bring her in and drop her off at the manse for a while so that I can work with her." She ran a hand fondly over Betsy's hair. "Someday this girl is going to college, Tom."

"Yes ma'am. I'm sure she will. She's sure smart enough for it." The smile he gave Betsy was intended to convey a private meaning but she did not indicate that she saw it.

"Well," said the teacher, beginning to feel a little uncomfortable, "I guess that's about it. I'll be getting back. Unless there's something you want me to do first?"

"Oh no, ma'am," said Tom, rejecting his dreams, "you've already done a lot. Yes sir. Me and Betsy will get along fine, won't we? Yes sir!"

"Well, then. Be a good girl, Elizabeth, and do everything

Mr. Wolsey tells you to. And mind, no acting up or running away. You know what happened last time!"

"What did she mean by that?" Tom asked as he led Betsy up to the house.

"You'll hear in the village. I was brought back by the police. They thought I was lost or something."

"Well," said Tom with a rare turn of phrase, "I was lost too without you. What made you run off like that?"

"You," said Betsy. "You lied to me. You said it wouldn't hurt and it did. I went off to see a doctor."

"I'm sorry," said Tom humbly, opening the screen door. "It won't hurt the next time."

"You're right," said Betsy, "because there isn't going to be a next time."

"Oh, come on!" he exclaimed, trying to put his arm around her. "I love you. We'll have great times together!"

"Not those kinds of times," said Betsy, looking around the front parlor with some distaste. "You've had your fun. I'm here because I can't go back to school and my parents and old Cushing made me come. But if you think you're going to do it whenever you like, you're wrong!"

Tom pulled her to him and tried to kiss her—but before he could reach her lips she jabbed him in the crotch. With a howl he doubled up on the floor.

"Why, you dirty little bitch!"

Betsy laughed, picked up her bundle and, stepping around him, started up the stairs. He tried to grab her, but nausea overcame him. As she explored the bedroom situation she could hear him vomiting over the front porch railing.

In the days that followed Tom found that she meant business. She got up when he did, made the meals, cleaned the house and, in the quiet hours, pored over her school books and any other reading matter she could get. She lived on the farm but her mind was out in the world beyond Eastwood, beyond Ontario, exploring, dreaming, planning. She had learned a good deal from her experience in Woodstock. The next time it would be different. The next time no one would bring her back.

About the only benefits Tom got out of the relationship were the better meals (she wasn't much of a cook yet but anything was better than his own efforts), the tidier house, and the realization that, in the eyes of his friends, he had somehow come off a hero.

It was hard to pin that down. Betsy had quite a name. The stories had got back from Woodstock about her adventure there and perhaps they had grown in re-telling. One thing that seemed to be accepted, possibly because the local folk wanted it to be true, was that she had, indeed, inherited a fortune. Some had even seen her cards—and it said so, right there in print. It was generally agreed that the money was on deposit in the bank in Woodstock.

Tom, who knew that what money she might have was his, was not inclined to argue. First, it could make him look a fool. And second, if the word got out that he had been playing around with her, her parents would be over in a flash to take her away. And even if she wasn't showing any signs of giving in as yet, there was always hope she'd weaken.

Meantime, every time he went into the village someone would say, "How's the heiress, Tom?" or "How's it feel to have someone wealthy like that working for you?" He was getting more attention from people than he had ever had before—and he loved it.

Once, he had to draw the line. Young Sam Draper greeted him at the store with, "Getting lots of young stuff these days?" and he hit him. That stopped that. No one else wanted a bloody nose. And Tom's righteous indignation (based on fact) seemed to convince everyone that, as had been her practice in the past, Betsy Bigley was still staying away from men.

Of an evening, Tom sometimes told her about what was being said. It seemed to please her. She looked particularly happy the night he reported that he had heard someone state that they knew for a fact that the reason she inherited the money was that she really wasn't a Bigley at all, but someone else's child that they had been hired to take and raise. (Tom didn't know that Betsy herself had whispered this to the minister's wife just the week before, after making the good lady promise not to tell a soul.)

Time flattened out. The weeks went by. The cold came down on the land. With crops in and the vegetable bins in the cellar loaded, Tom had more time indoors. Betsy looked ahead with apprehension to the days when the snow would be deep, too deep, and the two of them would be shut in from the world.

"Tom," she said one evening in the kitchen after he had had a good feed of pork hocks and cabbage and was ready for bed, "I've been thinking. Why don't we take a little trip? There's nothing much to do now until spring plowing except to keep the cattle fed. You could get someone to do that and milk and we could go off somewhere—maybe to London or even Toronto and have ourselves a time."

He looked up from unhooking the laces from his boots.

"What kind of a time?" he asked meaningfully.

Betsy turned from the water pail by the sink and waved the dipper like a wand. "Oh, see the big houses. The street-cars. Go to stores. Maybe a play. You know!"

"What would I want to do that for?" asked Tom, "I've seen a house. This one. And we haven't got the money to fool around stores."

42

His little housekeeper put down the dipper and knelt in front of him to help pull off his muddy boots.

"We could stay in a hotel," she whispered, her head bent. "Together."

Tom reached down and tipped up her chin so that he could see her face. "You mean—together? Like—like we was married?"

Betsy nodded. "Like we was married. Would you fancy that?"

Tom nodded. "You know I would!" He tried to slip his hands under her arms to lift her up, but she got to her feet quickly and stepped back. "What do you say?" she asked excitedly.

Tom considered the matter slowly. His loins were ready to start the trip that moment but, as usual, his mind was a little tardy. "I don't know," he said, shaking his head. "I don't think your parents would take to it. Besides, those cows don't like anyone else but me to milk them. They might go dry or something."

Betsy shrugged and went to the dishpan, "Well, of course, if you don't want me—"

Tom got up and put his big, rough hands on her shoulders. "You know I want you, Betsy, but why do we have to go somewhere else to do it?"

Betsy turned to face him. "Why? Because there's no way we're going to do it here, that's why. Suppose somebody came; Miss Cushing or somebody! You'd be in deep trouble, you know. But away from here, like over in London, there'd be nobody to know. It'd be like in another world."

Tom thought some more, kneading his hands. Finally, he said, "No. No, it's not right. You're too young for anybody to think you was my wife. Anyway, I haven't got that kind of money."

"You could borrow some on the farm."

"But I haven't paid that last loan yet."

"I've got money. Over in the bank in Woodstock. We could use that."

"No," he said firmly, "It still isn't right. Maybe next year."

Betsy looked at him coldly. "There won't be a next year," she said. "If you won't take me, I'm going on my own."

"Oh, no you're not," Tom replied brusquely. "You're not going anywhere for a while yet. You're staying right here, like you was told to do, for at least another year. If you don't, the police'll be after you to bring you back like they did last time."

Betsy glared at him, threw the dish towel in his face, and ran out of the room. Tom stared after her, feeling very unhappy. But he knew what was right—and that was that. Having his way with Betsy was one thing but going off to a city was quite another. His parents had brought him up well and he knew the difference between fun and sin.

Betsy knew he was right, too—and it made her angry. She had a tremendous contempt for facts. But it was true that she still looked too young to pose as his wife. And if she headed out on her own it was very likely that the police would be after her. There was nothing for it but to let winter happen. In the spring she would be older. Things would be different.

She built a cocoon of books and magazines around herself and settled down to wait. The long nights crept by. Once in a while she was able to get home to see her family, but it wasn't the same anymore. Only her father seemed unchanged. After each visit she would return to the Wolsey farm and dream that he had come to rescue her. Some nights, he came with his horse and cutter just to carry her home. Other nights—the really good ones—he came to tell her that he had decided to move into Woodstock or to London and was taking her with him. In one great dream he arrived all

44

excited to tell her that his brother in England had died and that they were all going to sail there to the funeral. On the boat, she met a very rich man who fell madly in love with her and took her to his castle. As a result, she never did get to the funeral. When she woke up she felt badly about that because she knew she had once again disappointed her father.

Well, she had been made to seem a fool over that Woodstock affair, but she would show them. Someday, instead of that hurt look in her father's eyes, there would be pride. Someday. Someday soon.

CHAPTER TWO

I n early spring, the cocoon burst. It was time to be going. Tom was beginning to be too much to stand. It wasn't even fun to tease him anymore by letting him get little glimpses as she bathed or by accidentally brushing against him on the way to bed. Oh, it was effective. She could often hear him in the night as his bed creaked with the strain of his self-releasing rhythm. But it wasn't fun any longer.

Miss Cushing bored her too. At the manse, she kept trying to recapture their old intimacy. At the Wolsey place, she couldn't take her eyes off Tom.

Betsy found an old, battered travelling bag in a storage cupboard under the eaves and began to use it to carry her books. One day when Tom let her off at the manse, Betsy waited on the stoop until he had driven away, then walked over to the railway station and locked herself in the outhouse.

It was bitterly cold in there. She thought she was going to freeze. But finally the train came. She waited until the conductor had cried, "Board!" and swung himself up on the step; then she burst out of the privy and ran across the platform, her valise swinging behind her. He lifted her onto the train as it began to move.

"Thank you," she gasped. "Oh! Oh no!"

"What's the matter, miss?" he asked, lowering the flap over the steps and closing the door.

"My purse! I—I left my purse in the—you know. With all my money in it!" She began to cry.

"Now, now. It will be all right," the conductor assured her, patting her shoulder. "You just go in and sit down. And when we get to Woodstock I'll telegraph back and get the station master to go get it and send it on. How far are you going?"

"To London. My uncle is meeting me. Is it all right if he pays for my ticket?"

"Sure it is. Now you just dry your eyes and relax."

"Oh, thank you, sir!" Betsy smiled bravely through her tears. "I'll be sure to tell my father what a nice man you are."

She went into the nearest coach. It was empty save for one man sitting about halfway down. He was trying hard to read a paper despite the jerking of the train. Betsy went down the aisle, put her bag up on the metal rack, and sat down opposite him.

He glanced over and smiled, then noticed the tears which she had not removed.

"Is something wrong?"

She told him her purse story. The touch of having left it in the unmentionable place was good, she thought. It had to be true. No lady would refer to being in an outhouse if she could avoid it.

The conductor passed by, lighting the overhead lamps. "Feeling better?" She nodded miserably.

"It's a long ride to London," the man said. "What are you going to eat?"

"I left my sandwiches in—with my purse."

"Well, don't worry," he said comfortingly, reaching across the aisle and patting her knee, "we can get you something when the train stops at Woodstock."

"Thank you," she said humbly.

The man returned to his paper, holding it close in the dim light. Betsy leaned back in the green padded seat and watched him out of the corner of her eye.

Some sort of business man. Maybe a traveller. About forty. Not bad looking, just a little fat. She wanted to reach over and loosen his collar. There was a big gold ring on the hand nearest to her and on the bulging vest jiggled a watch chain that looked as though it might be real gold.

A couple of times he glanced over and smiled. Betsy began to shiver and pulled her coat around her.

"Cold?"

She nodded.

"These coaches are never warm enough. Why don't you move over beside me and I'll put my coat over both of us?"

He stood up and flipped the back of the seat in front of him so that the two seats faced each other.

"There," he said, "now we can put our feet up and be real cozy."

Betsy sat down between him and the window and he spread his great wollen overcoat over their legs.

"Better?"

She smiled.

"How old are you?"

"Sixteen."

"Still go to school?"

"I'm going to London to be a nurse."

"Great! I think that's wonderful!" He put his hand on her leg under the coat. "That's a fine profession. I'll bet you know a lot already about nursing and things like that."

"Only what I've read," Betsy said modestly, feeling the warmth of his hand. "I've still got a lot to learn—if only someone will teach me." She looked up innocently into his eyes. Gray, she noted. The first gray eyes she had ever seen.

He squeezed her leg.

"Well now, it happens I know a little bit about such things. Oh," he said modestly, "I'm not a doctor or anything, but I've been around, know what I mean?" Again, a squeeze. This time a little higher.

Betsy nodded. "I guess when a girl's an only child raised on the farm away from, well, boys and everything, you don't know much. This is my first time away from home. I really don't know what's ahead. Are you from London, Mr—?"

"Rafferty. Joshua Rafferty. Call me Josh." He turned slightly on his side toward her and in doing so his hand slid up under the overcoat as far as Betsy hoped it would go for the moment. It was a long trip. "No, I'm from Toronto. I travel in woollen goods. A man of the cloth, you might say, eh?" He chuckled at his standard joke.

They chatted on, and what with the motion of the train and his occasional slight shiftings on the seat, she soon became aware of his hip pressing against hers.

His teeth were yellow and there was a smell of old tobacco on his clothes. But the watch chain did look real. She tried not to stare at it.

When the train pulled into Woodstock he got off and

bought her a sandwich. She noticed how quickly he returned and how anxiously he examined the coach as he came in to see if their privacy had been invaded. He was obviously relieved that the few who had gotten on had chosen the other coaches.

The sandwich was a sad, stale snack but she made the best of it.

"Now," he said when she had finished and the coat was once more in place, "let's talk some more about nursing. The human body is a wonderful thing, isn't it?"

"I don't know. I mean, I don't know much about it," said Betsy shyly.

"Well, we're all pretty much the same," said Josh. "You're a girl and I'm a man. That is the only difference. You've seen yourself—and you've seen a man, haven't you?"

Betsy shook her head. "Not—like that."

"No? Well maybe I can help."

"Oh, would you?" cried Betsy. "It's terrible to be so ignorant!"

"No, it's not. Look, I'm an older man, old enough to be your father, right? If I show you the difference, it's just to help you be a better nurse, right?"

Betsy nodded. Josh glanced around to see if the conductor was coming, then raised the overcoat.

"Well, look. See that? That's what the difference is all about."

Betsy peered under the coat and saw that somehow he had managed to unbutton himself.

"Is that your—?"

"That's right," he smiled. "Would you like to feel it? Go ahead, I don't mind."

Betsy put her hand around it. There wasn't much to hold. Surprising in such a big man, she thought.

"It gets harder when you pull on it," he explained. He was right.

When they reached London, she got ready to leave the train. She was peering out of the window when the conductor came along.

"See your uncle?"

Betsy shook her head. "He may not have gotten back from Toronto in time," she said. "He has an office there."

"Well," said Josh, "why don't you stay on to Toronto and meet him there?"

"Oh, I couldn't!" Betsy protested. "The conductor has been good enough to trust me this far . . ."

"Well, that's right," said Josh, "but I'll tell you what. Let me pay your fare from here to Toronto then you'll just owe him to Woodstock. I guess the railway could stand that, eh Conductor?"

It was time to open the coach doors. The conductor hesitated, grinned, and walked away. Betsy and Josh settled back with their feet up and her instructor replaced his handy overcoat.

Toronto was bigger than she had dreamed. The streets were all lit with lamps on tall poles and there was a raised place to walk along the sides. Having been rather easily persuaded to wait and look for her uncle in the morning, Betsy accompanied her new friend to a hotel near the station.

It was a much larger hotel than the one in Woodstock but, she thought, not nearly as nice.

"This is where I live," Josh explained. "Not much of a room, I guess, but it's cheap."

"You don't have a home?" Betsy asked.

"Nope. See, I'm a travelling man. I keep this room here as a base. But most of the time I'm on the road, covering my territory."

"It must be a lonely way to live."

"Well," he admitted, "a lot of the time it is, but tonight will make up for a lot of that!"

His room was indeed small and dingy. Whatever he paid didn't seem to include cleaning services. In the light from the coal oil lamp he lit by the bed, Betsy could see a bulging cupboard, cracked walls, and a bureau piled high with old magazines.

Since he was obviously anxious to get to bed and that meant undressing, she looked around for a place to put her clothes and finally had to settle for piling them neatly on top of her bag.

When she woke up in the morning he was still asleep and snoring, flat on his back with his mouth open. Moving carefully, she slipped out of bed and quietly put on her clothes. His trousers were flung over a bedpost at the foot. The wallet in his hip pocket wasn't very thick, but there was enough in it to start her off. After that she could always unpin the rest of Tom's money from inside the back of her bloomers.

She gingerly lifted his vest from the doorknob and removed his watch and chain. Until now, she had never had a watch. This was a nice gold one with a lid all engraved with little flowers. Much too nice for a man like that to be carrying. She snapped open the lid and saw that it was after seven.

Beset by a great desire to relieve herself, she paused by the wash stand but decided it was too risky to use the pot. She eased the room door open and crept out. Once in the hall, with the door shut, she paused to open her bag and remove her purse.

There was a much better looking hotel across the street. It rose a full four floors above her. The gold letters along the edge of the balcony over the entrance read "The Queen's

Hotel." She noted with pleasure that it even had a doorman. As he opened the big oak door for her, she turned to him.

"I am meeting my uncle for breakfast. Hiram T. Snelgrove of New York. Has he come down yet?"

"I couldn't say, Miss. But you could ask at the desk."

"Thank you. Could you keep this bag for me until after we've eaten? And where may I freshen up?"

The doorman took her battered little valise and directed her to a room at the rear. It was a charming room and she almost forgot her urgency as she admired the marble sinks and played with the taps.

Some minutes later she emerged considerably refreshed and—with the aid of the comb and hairpins she carried in her purse—at least two years older.

As the waiter seated her at breakfast, she looked at him sharply. "You're new here, aren't you? What's your name?"

"Oh no, ma'am. I've worked here since this place opened in '62. My Name is Henry."

"Really? I'm sorry, then, that I did not recognize you, Henry. Of course, I keep confusing this dining room with the one in the Louvre in Paris. Now tell me, what would you recommend?"

When the meal was over, Betsy put her purse on the table and went out. The clerk at the desk told her that there was no Hiram T. Snelgrove registered.

"Oh dear!" Betsy exclaimed. "I do hope that they didn't attach his car to the wrong train! That happened once before, you know. Uncle Hiram was supposed to go to Palm Beach to visit his friend, Henry Flagler. When he woke up he was in Chicago. I guess you could hear him back in New York! You know how men like that are."

"Yes ma'am, I do indeed," the sympathetic little clerk assured her. He had had his share of displeased tycoons.

53

"However," Betsy went on, "I'm sure he'll be in on today's train. He and Mr. Eaton are having dinner tonight. That's why he asked me to join him, so that Mrs. Eaton could have company."

"Timothy Eaton?"

Betsy nodded. "Uncle Hiram is very interested in Mr. Eaton's store. My uncle buys things like stores and hotels. As a matter of fact, the last time I saw him he said he was thinking of buying this nice place of yours. Well," she sighed, "I guess there's nothing for me to do but wait." She looked doubtfully at the hard-seated, high-backed, wooden chairs along the walls of the lobby.

"Would you like a room, Miss?" the clerk asked helpfully. "It will be some hours before the train from New York gets in."

"Well, perhaps that would be best," said Betsy.

The clerk reached for his register. "And what name shall I record?" he asked.

Betsy wanted to say "Vanessa" because that was the name of her favorite love story heroine at the time, but she was afraid he might ask her to spell it. It was annoying, being Vanessa and not being able to remember whether there was one "s" or two.

"Elizabeth Cunard," she said primly, adding, "of London."

"London, Ontario?" the clerk asked routinely as he wrote.

"You mean you have a London here?" exclaimed Betsy, raising her eyebrows. "How quaint!"

"Yes, ma'am. It's quite a large city, really. Well, here's your key. Oh, do you have any bags?"

Betsy nodded. "Just one old thing with my evening dress in it. I left the others on our boat. The doorman has it. Would you have someone bring it up? I'm afraid I left my purse at the breakfast table, excuse me." She turned away and then came back. "Oh, and thank you for offering me the room! I know my uncle will be very pleased with your attitude."

She went back into the dining room and sat down. The account for the meal was waiting beside her purse. She beckoned the waiter. "I assume I may charge this to my room —and the gratuity as well?"

The waiter nodded and offered her his pencil.

"Excellent," said Betsy, signing 'Miss Cunard' with a flourish, "but I do think I would enjoy another cup of your rather good coffee."

When she came out of the dining room again the clerk came from behind his desk. "I'm afraid the boy who runs the lift has gone on an errand," he said. "Allow me." He pulled back the sliding door of a gilded cage and waited. Betsy looked at the barred box nervously. Why did he want her in there? It looked suspiciously like a jail cell.

"It's perfectly safe," he assured her. "Ours is the first hotel in Canada to have one," he added proudly.

With some misgivings, she stepped inside. He promptly joined her and the door slid shut with a clang. The room gave a jolt and started to move up. Betsy gasped.

"Sure beats walking!" the clerk exclaimed with a grin. "I suppose all the hotels in London have them?"

Betsy watched through the bars as the lobby disappeared below. "What? Oh yes, yes, all the better hotels."

"I guess you could say The Queen's is the finest hotel in Canada," the clerk commented as he ran a finger lovingly along the polished brass grill-work of the door. "We're the first to have this, the first to have a furnace for heating instead of stoves and fireplaces, and the first to have rooms that have their very own private baths. It's a real up-to-date place."

"It certainly seems that way," Betsy agreed, as the cage

jerked to a stop flush with a floor. "I guess that's why my uncle likes it."

The clerk slid back the door and she stepped out with a smile of thanks that was painted on to hide the fact that she had just had a very bad fright.

The little man led the way down the hall and opened a door for her. "Here you are, Miss!" he exclaimed, standing back and holding out the key. Betsy had the feeling that, with even the slightest encouragement, he would be willing to step inside for a while. But that did not suit her current purpose and she already had what she wanted from him.

However, as insurance, she gave him a warm and personal smile as she accepted the key.

Once inside with the door closed, she was torn by three desires; to get out and see the city, to catch up on the sleep she had lost to the surprisingly virile travelling salesman, and to climb into the long, white bathtub and just soak for a while. "Well," she thought, "it's still too early for the stores to open and I can't go to bed with my clothes on or they'll be even more wrinkled, so I might as well undress, have a bath and then rest a while."

It was noon when she woke up. Tom would be wanting his breakfast. The thought almost threw her out of bed, for she had no desire to have him come tramping upstairs to tell her. And then she looked around at the big hotel room. There was no Tom. There wouldn't ever be a Tom again! She relaxed and stretched like a kitten, feeling the smoothness of the sheets, smelling the freshness of the linen, absorbing the luxury of escape.

After a moment, she got up and explored. The window had heavy drapes that hung to the floor. Velvet, she decided. They were held back by loops of heavy cord. Silk. Over a little writing desk of dark wood there hung a picture of a

rural scene. She peered at the title printed on the border—
Morning In Westphalia. Well, wherever Westphalia was, it
didn't look much like any mornings she had known! Next
came a high bureau of the same dark wood. She opened all
the drawers hopefully, but no one had left anything. Her
circuit brought her to the clothes closet and she was facing
her dress. It looked terrible. No one staying in a room as nice
as this would wear a dress like that. Especially the niece of
Hiram T. Snelgrove.

She put it on and looked at herself in the mirror that
panelled the closet door. Well, there wasn't much you could
do. She got a hand towel, rolled it and tucked it into the
bodice. That helped a bit. The improvised bosom felt a little
rough on her breasts which were still tender from the working over they had been given the night before, but it did give
her a better, maturer profile. However, she would have to get
some better clothes right away.

Betsy went downstairs and paused at the desk. The clerk
smiled, "Resting comfortably?"

"Quite," said Betsy. "However, I think I shall get some air.
What time will my uncle's train be in?"

"Oh, not for another three hours," the clerk assured her.
"You have plenty of time for a stroll."

"I hope so," said Betsy, "I wouldn't want to miss being
here when he arrives." She paused. "By the way, I do hope you
have a nice suite reserved for him. He's very particular, you
know."

"Well, we have nothing marked down for him at the moment, but there is no problem. If he is expecting a suite, we
can give him our best. The new Governor-General, Lord
Lisgar, has stayed in it," the clerk added proudly, "so now
we call it the Regal Suite."

"That should do," said Betsy. "As a matter of fact, there is no need for me to tie up an extra room for you. Why don't you just have the maid put my bag in Uncle Hiram's suite and I'll go there to await him when I return?"

"Thank you, Miss," said the clerk, appreciatively, "we are going to be a little short of single rooms this evening."

About half an hour later—for it took Betsy a while to find the telegraph office and acquire some forms—a telegram was delivered to the hotel. It was signed H.T. Snelgrove and it read, "Please reserve best suite and hold pending my arrival. Delayed by breakdown my private car. Would appreciate any courtesies extended my niece, Miss Cunard. Ask her to contact T. Eaton and apologize my non-arrival today."

Having taken care of her accommodation problem, Betsy turned her mind to clothing. Since that would require money, she did what she now knew that every sensible person did; she went to a bank. Choosing the one nearest Mr. Eaton's large store, she went in, marched up to a clerk and asked to see the manager.

The clerk might have hesitated had she not been so firm and commanding in her request. As it was, he was glad he had complied promptly when he heard her say as he ushered her in, "Good afternoon. I am Elizabeth Cunard of London. Mr. Eaton has told me that you are a good banker."

In a few minutes she and the manager emerged from his office and the manager, exuding the charm he saved for customers, ordered the clerk to open an account for her.

"It's just a temporary account," he told the clerk. "Miss Cunard is here in connection with her uncle's estate. She is staying at the Queen's. In the Regal Suite," he added significantly.

"Yes, sir," said the clerk, indicating that he had the message. Betsy opened her purse and brought out the check book she had acquired during her Woodstock foray. "Well," she sighed, "I suppose I really should put something into my account now that I have it. Banking is such a mystery! Do I make out the check to myself or to you?"

"To us will be fine, Miss Cunard," the manager answered. The clerk reached under the brass mesh of his window, passing her his pen freshly dipped in ink.

"I don't think I'll need much while I'm here," Betsy mused aloud. "Why don't I just put in, say, ten thousand?"

"Whatever you wish will be fine," the manager assured her. "Mr. Stephens, give Miss Cunard one of our check books so that she can draw on her account."

Betsy smiled at him and touched his cheek gently with her hand. "Mr. Eaton was right. You are a nice man!"

The clerk, after years of watching the financial cannibal bark and growl, was delighted to see his boss blush. It would be something to remember, he reflected and, as a result, didn't think to question why the niece of Samuel Cunard would have a check book for an account in the little town of Woodstock.

She thanked them both and left, feeling much happier and securer now that she had some money to spend. (The money pinned to her bloomers wasn't for spending, it was hers.) Not unnaturally, she took her first business to Mr. Eaton's store. It was the least she could do.

The lady in the dress department was sorry to hear of her loss. To arrive in a strange country only to be told that your wardrobe trunk had been allowed to fall overboard while the ship was unloading had to be very upsetting. And she was sympathetic over Miss Cunard's embarrassment at having to admit that it had happened on one of her uncle's own ships.

"If it hadn't been for the kindness of my maid in letting me borrow this," Betsy confessed, indicating her dress, "I wouldn't be able to go out at all. I must say, I don't know styles here. Would you be good enough to help me pick out the right things to wear?"

An hour later a complete wardrobe was piled on the counter, Betsy was wearing a new dress, and the saleslady was almost purring as she made up the bill. "Will this be cash, Miss Cunard?" she asked.

"Oh heavens!" Betsy exclaimed, "My uncle would never allow me to charge anything! He doesn't believe that women know how to handle accounts!" She gave the clerk a woman-to-woman smile. "No, I'll give you a check on our account here. It's one Mr. Eaton helped me set up. Then, if you don't mind, I would appreciate it if you could have a boy take everything down to the Queen's for me. Tell him to put it in the Regal Suite. And, if you would, please be sure to ask him to tell the maid to hang up the dresses right away. They're much too pretty to get creased!" She brought out her new check book and borrowed the clerk's pen. "I do hope he can take them right away," she added. "As soon as I finish shopping, I must get back to the suite and dress for dinner. Mr. Eaton's carriage is calling for me early so that I can see something of your exciting city before we dine."

She handed the woman the check and turned to go. Then came "the clincher," as later students of her style were to call it. "May I ask you a personal question?" she asked, turning back. The saleslady nodded and leaned across the counter to hear as Betsy said softly, "I really should take Mrs. Eaton some little thing. Some little token. Now, I'm sure you've seen her a great deal and you know the kinds of things she likes. Of course, it couldn't be anything from the store. That wouldn't be a real present, would it? But there must be another store that would have something suitable, a little ring or brooch or something?"

"Well," said the clerk, the check in her hand forgotten for

the moment in the face of the flattery of someone believing that she—who had never seen Mrs. Eaton—would know what the owner's wife liked, "there's Ryrie's. It's one of the finest jewellery stores around. Of course," she added doubtfully, "it's a little expensive."

Betsy smiled. "Not by British standards, I'm sure! I wonder, do you suppose Mr. Eaton would mind if you asked the boy who is taking this clothing to the suite to stop there and pick up whatever I buy? I don't like to be burdened down."

"Of course," said the clerk. "It's just down Yonge Street a couple of blocks. You can't miss it."

Betsy felt a lot better going into Ryrie's. The new dress was definitely the kind of thing a well-to-do young lady in her early twenties should be wearing. And it was long enough to hide the fact that in her eagerness to be among jewellery she had not stopped to replace the rather worn and certainly girlish shoes with which she had left Tom's farm.

Once inside the big brass doors, she faltered for a moment as the solemnity of the dignified old firm came like a wave from behind its mahogany and glass counters and tried to flush out the young pretender. She half turned to leave—and then she remembered who she was and, pulling her thin shoulders back, faced the nearest counter and said to the gray-haired man behind it, "I am Sir Samuel Cunard's niece. Are you the manager?"

The little man looked shocked. "Oh no, ma'am! I expect you'd want to see Mr. Ryrie himself. Unfortunately, he is not in today. But," he hesitated and gathered his courage, "I wonder if I could be of some assistance?"

"Perhaps," said Betsy doubtfully, "I just need a few things. Do you know Mrs. Eaton?"

"Mrs. Timothy Eaton? Oh yes, ma'am. That is, to see. She comes in here occasionally."

"Well, good," said Betsy, brightening, "then you're probably just the person I should have asked for in the first place! I am going to be their guest for the weekend and I want to take her something. Perhaps a brooch or a little necklace. But nothing too expensive," she cautioned, "I wouldn't want to spend more than a hundred or two on it."

The clerk rubbed his nose to hide his excitement. "Well now, let me see." He began to pull out trays of brooches and bracelets and various types of necklaces.

Betsy felt her heart grow warm at the sight of all that beauty. "And what about rings?" she asked, trying to control her voice. "Perhaps she'd like a ring!"

He added some trays of rings to the array.

Betsy went over each item carefully, holding the ones with stones up to the light to see the sparkle, rubbing the gold mountings with a loving finger.

"Oh, I'd love to take them all!" she exclaimed.

"Well, they're all for sale," laughed the clerk.

"That! That one there!" Betsy cried, lifting up a large ring. It had a deep red ruby surrounded by little diamonds. "How much?"

"I'm afraid it's more than you had in mind," said the clerk. "Five hundred and fifty. Besides," he added honestly, "I think it's a little, well, showy for a weekend gift. It's more like an engagement ring."

"Yes, isn't it?" mused Betsy. "Well, I think I'll take it anyway. For myself. And this necklace," she added, picking up a thin gold strand from which hung a single teardrop pearl. "How much is it?"

"That's not a real pearl, of course," the clerk warned. "But the necklace is eighteen karat. Forty-five dollars."

"And this little brooch here? I think that would do nicely for Mrs. Eaton, don't you?"

"Yes, it would," he agreed. "However, those are good

quality sapphires. I'm afraid our price is two hundred and fifty on that."

"Fine," said Betsy carelessly, "but do box it separately for me, will you? Now, what does all that come to?" She pulled out her check book as he made up the bill. Reading upside down, a trick she had developed by looking over her shoulder during exams, she had the total written on the check almost as soon as he had written it on the bill.

Handing him the check, she said, "Now, if you don't mind, I'm not going to take these things with me. I have some other shopping to do and I might lose them. Mr. Eaton will send a boy around for them shortly, if that's all right."

"Oh certainly, Miss Cunard," said the clerk, "We'll have everything all wrapped and waiting."

"Thank you," said Betsy, "and do tell Mr. Ryrie I was sorry to have missed meeting him."

The next stop was a shoe store. It was soon obvious that the Cunard name meant nothing there, but she made such a scene about refusing to buy unless they could promise to have the three pairs she had chosen delivered to the Regal Suite by five that, in the confusion, her check wasn't questioned.

"Now, what else do I need?" she asked herself as she emerged from the shoe store. She glanced up and down the street and saw her answer. In a row, almost side by side, were a steamship office, a leather goods store, and a little shop whose sign said that it offered trinkets.

Within a very short while she had obtained, without charge, some Cunard trunk labels, had arranged for the delivery of a wardrobe trunk to Hiram Snelgrove at his suite, and had bought an inexpensive wedding band.

She didn't really know why she wanted the latter. But since Ryrie's was contributing an engagement ring, it might be a handy thing to have sometime as an adjunct.

As she was passing Ryrie's, she glanced at the clock which

stood in its wrought iron standard on the pavement. It was time to get back to the hotel.

Yes, said the clerk, they had heard from her uncle. He read her the telegram. They agreed that it was very unfortunate that her uncle had been delayed. Yes, her things had been moved to the Regal Suite. Certainly, he would be glad to send up any parcels that came.

Betsy took the key to the suite from him and went up full of anticipation. But the suite wasn't really very regal. She had expected that the parlor would at least have a small throne. It was nice, there was no denying that. It even had a square, fat-legged coffin of a piano. But no throne, no gold and crystal candelabra, no paintings on the ceiling. She shrugged away her disappointment, explored the bedroom, and noted that if the bed didn't have a canopy like the one under which Henry the Eighth had died in her English History book, at least it had high posts which, she supposed, was something. In the bathroom she grabbed a towel and wrapped it around her head just as the knocker on the suite door banged.

"Miss Cunard?" asked the messenger boy from Eaton's from behind his armload of boxes.

"The madam is not home," said Betsy primly.

"Well," said the boy, passing her his load, "I'm to tell you the dresses are to be hung up right away."

"Thank you," said Betsy firmly, closing the door in his face.

She spent the rest of the day playing with her new toys, trying on the dresses, admiring the necklace, the brooch and the rings, walking about carefully to get the feel of the shoes when they arrived—and then putting everything into the wardrobe trunk after she had plastered it with Cunard stickers. At eight, having bathed and put on one of the new dresses, she rang for a maid, asked her to unpack the trunk, and went down to dinner feeling very much in possession of herself.

Waiters work long hours she observed, as the man who had seated her at breakfast nodded his recognition respectfully. To the man in black at the door of the dining room she said, "Could you put me at one of Henry's tables, please?"

"Certainly, Miss Cunard," he replied politely.

Betsy marvelled at the internal communication system of the hotel. It was a nice touch, knowing her name.

"Good evening, Henry."

"Good evening, Miss."

The menu he handed her was a big piece of cardboard covered with items listed in French as well as English. Betsy could see at a glance that there wasn't a thing offered that she recognized.

"Ah me," she sighed prettily, "tell me, Henry, if you were dining alone in a hotel whose chef you don't know, what would you order?"

"Well, Miss, in this hotel you can't go far wrong with fish, if that's your pleasure. We have, if I may say so, something of a reputation in that respect. Tonight, you might enjoy the baked pickerel. It comes with a nice egg sauce."

Betsy nodded and handed him back the menu. "Then that's what I'll have," she decided, wondering as she said it why it was considered necessary to hide a local dish like that behind a French name. Perhaps it meant that you could charge more.

"Shall I send the wine steward?" Henry asked.

"Oh no, thanks," said Betsy, "I do not drink spirits." She could not explain the truth; that she had never had the chance. Her family would not have permitted wine or liquor in the home even if they could have afforded it. And, having read many a story on the evil ways of John Barleycorn, Betsy had no desire to have her mind muddled by getting into his grasp.

She was doing fine, just fine. It had been a glorious day and now here she was in a smart dress and new shoes, her hair piled high, a beautiful necklace riding on her bosom, and an even more beautiful ring on her finger, dining in a high-ceilinged room filled with well-dressed people just like that Frenchwoman, Jeanne de Valois, a hundred years before.

There were, of course, a few things she had to think through. She knew enough about banking to believe that it would take a minimum of two days for the check she had deposited at the bank to get to Woodstock and come back rejected. That meant that she was reasonably safe in that regard for another day. But she was a little concerned because she had let herself develop one uncle too many. Either Samuel Cunard or Hiram T. Snelgrove had to go. It was a pity, because she was fond of them both. However, if anyone were to look at it logically, it wasn't likely that she could be the niece of both without anyone ever having heard of her before. If the police got involved it would be very easy for them to contact the Cunard family and blow apart her story on that relationship—and even easier to ascertain that dear old Uncle Hiram was living only in her mind.

Of the two men, she thought she liked Uncle Hiram the better. What was the word some writer had used in writing about his heroine? That was it; Uncle Hiram was so *malleable*. Betsy had looked it up in Miss Cushing's dictionary. You could mold Uncle Hiram into anything you wanted him to be. The late steamship magnate was too fixed and firm; everyone knew what he was like.

Over the soup, Betsy pondered what to do with Uncle Hiram. It was clearly up to him to get her out of the hotel by the following night. Paying the bill would be no problem; she could write another check. But where should she go? Perhaps he would send for her to join him in New York! She felt a thrill at the thought—and then reason prevailed; she was not yet ready for New York. From Eastwood to a night

of thrashing around in a run-down hotel to this was great—
and a great deal. But New York! It was so big! Besides, she
wasn't sure that they would let her cross the border. She
needed more information on that.

The pickerel was pickerel. No amount of egg sauce and
parsley decoration could disguise the familiar fish. The only
difference from the way it was served at home was that it
wasn't fried in leftover bacon grease. For that she was thank-
ful.

Should Uncle Hiram die and leave her some money? No,
that would take longer to handle than she had. Besides, she
was a bit tired of inheritances. It would be more fun to work
it out some other way.

However, there was nothing wrong with having Uncle
Hiram die. He is aboard his private car, on his way to meet
her when, suddenly, he has a heart attack. His faithful servant, Caspar, does his best to revive him, but there isn't a
doctor aboard and the train rushes on through the night with
the other passengers unaware that in the shiny car at the rear
one of the great men of America has breathed his last.

The picture of the lonely death was so vivid in her mind
that Betsy felt a tear start down her cheek. She brushed it
away with the back of her hand.

A quiet male voice said, "Excuse me, is anything wrong?"

Through moist eyes she saw that the man eating by himself at the table on her left was leaning toward her solicitously.

Even as she summoned a brave smile, she took in the
quality of his attire, the precision with which his cravat was
tied, the iron gray of his hair, the refinement in his lined
face, the kindness in the eyes that were on her.

"I'm all right, thank you," she said softly, dabbing at her
eyes with her napkin. "I'm afraid I've just had some rather
bad news."

The man raised an inquiring eyebrow. "Oh? I'm sorry to

hear that. If you would care to tell me about it, may I join you?"

Betsy nodded. The man signalled to Henry to transfer his coffee and moved over to sit opposite her.

"What has happened?" he asked gently as Henry refilled their cups.

Betsy waited until the waiter was gone.

"I—I came here from London to meet my uncle." She paused uncertainly, "If you're not from the United States you probably haven't heard of him—Hiram T. Snelgrove? The railway magnate?"

"Of course," said the man, and Betsy thought "Watch it!"

"Well," she went on, "he is—was—on his way here to pick me up in his private car. I've just had a telephone message that he has had a heart attack." Her voice fell to a whisper and her eyes began to fill again at the thought. "All alone in that car. Nobody but his faithful servant, Caspar, to care, to hold his hand. It's an awful way to die."

The man was silent for a moment, his eyes on the tablecloth. "Yes, yes it is," he agreed. "And yet, you know," he said looking up, "for a man like Hiram T. Snelgrove perhaps it's not as bad as you think. A rugged individualist, it's a safe bet that he would want to maintain his dignity even in death. I don't fancy he'd have wanted a big fuss."

This is amazing, said Betsy to herself, this man knows Uncle Hiram as well as I do!

"The terrible thing is," she said, "and I know this sounds selfish, but I feel cheated. I had never met Uncle Hiram and having come all this way . . . They are taking the car off at Syracuse and sending it back to New York City. I'll never see him now, alive or dead!" She paused. "Tell me, if you knew him, what was he really like, Mr. ———?"

"Oh, sorry. I'm Jeff Snyder, Miss . . .?"

"Miss Cunard, Elizabeth Cunard. Was he a kindly man?"

There was just a flick and a pause—caused, Betsy knew, by her Cunard canard—and then Mr. Snyder nodded. "I think it's safe to say that. Mind you," he added quickly, "I didn't know him well. I'm in real estate development; we lived in different worlds. But we did see each other once in a while. At one point I thought of letting him become a director of one of my companies, but he always seemed so busy with his little railroads that I changed my mind. You say your name is Cunard? If yours is the steamship family, you'll understand how I felt."

Betsy nodded. "That's why I had to grow up before I met him. My uncle Samuel would have nothing to do with him. But with Uncle Samuel gone and the estate divided up amongst us, I suddenly realized that I was free to go where I wanted to go and to do what I wanted to do. And one of the things I wanted to do very much was to get acquainted with Uncle Hiram. I was his only living relative, you know." She paused and sighed. No matter how she tried, it always seemed to come back to inheritances. "Now," she went on with a little bitterness in her voice, "I suppose it will be just like when Uncle Samuel died; lawyers all over the place and decisions to make. I know so little about money," she added frankly.

"Well," said Mr. Snyder judiciously, "it is true that there is a lot to know. Perhaps what you need is a manager; somebody to act for you and look after all that sort of thing. You're much too young and pretty to have to worry about such matters."

Betsy acknowledged his compliment with a little smile. "Perhaps you're right. But I don't know anyone like that, especially here in Canada—and I need help right now, this very minute."

Snyder leaned forward. "Why right now?" he asked huskily.

"Because of who I am," said Betsy simply. "Tomorrow the

story will be in all the papers. 'Steamship Heiress Inherits Railway Fortune.' I'm registered here in the Regal Suite under my own name; the reporters will be pounding on the door and all sorts of—of opportunists will be trying to see me. And here I am, all alone and undefended!"

Snyder took a sip of coffee. "Would you let me help? I know we've only just met, but perhaps a man in my position could make thinks easier. Given a few days, I might even be able to find that manager for you."

"Oh, would you?" Betsy reached out and put her little hand—the one with the ruby ring—on his arm. He glanced down almost imperceptibly and then nodded.

"The first thing to do," he said in a businesslike way, "is to protect your privacy. I think you should move to another hotel and register under another name."

"But isn't that dishonest?" Betsy protested.

"Not really. Famous people do it all the time just so that they won't be bothered. We'll spirit you away tonight. To-morrow, as it happens, I have to be in New York anyway. If you will give me a letter authorizing me to act for you, I'll contact Snelgrove's office, find out who his lawyers are, tell them where you are and get everything cleared up. You'll probably want to be there for the funeral, so I'll tell them to have any papers that need signing ready by then. We'll get the will read and all that and you'll be free to leave New York the following day."

"You make it sound so simple!" Betsy sighed.

"It's just normal procedure for a business man," Snyder said with a disparaging smile. "And the least I can do for a damsel in distress. As a matter of fact," he brought out and consulted a thin gold watch, "if I am to add Snelgrove's lawyers to my calls in New York, I really must be sure to catch tonight's train. Would you like to come to my room and write that letter?"

Betsy lowered her eyes modestly. "Perhaps you should come to mine—I mean to Uncle Hiram's. The Regal Suite on the top floor."

Snyder nodded. "All right. Why don't you go up and start packing? I'll just attend to the waiter and be right up."

The writing of the letter did not take long with Mr. Snyder dictating. Betsy did not know what the phrase "power of attorney" meant, but she had the feeling that her newly-found friend had a very clear understanding of what was going on, as he saw it, and that Elizabeth Cunard was signing away a great deal.

"And now for the quiet exit!" her rescuer exclaimed as soon as the ink had dried and the letter was in his pocket. "I'll escort you to the door and put you in a cab. But tell the driver to wait. I'll go to the desk and explain why you've had to leave and tell them to bill your uncle's office. Then I'll have your trunk brought down and you'll be off."

"But where should I go?" Betsy asked helplessly.

"Tell the driver to take you to the Seneca House. It's a small, quiet hotel where you won't be disturbed. You can use my name, if you like. Call yourself Mrs. Snyder. I will telegraph you as soon as I know when your uncle's funeral is going to be."

Betsy nodded and they went downstairs. Before long, a porter appeared with her trunk, Snyder came to the door of the hotel to wave good-bye, and the hansom started off.

"Where to, Miss?" the driver asked.

"The railway station, please," said Betsy.

The driver muttered something to himself and, turning the horse, pulled up in front of the station which was just across the street.

"My goodness," said Betsy, "I didn't realize it was so close!"

"That's all right, Miss," said the driver, "though most people do walk across."

The next train scheduled to leave, she saw on a big board, was for London and Detroit. Mr. Snyder's train for New York didn't leave for another hour. She went into the ladies' toilet and extracted from under her skirts enough money to get her to London. She was sorry to be leaving Toronto, but with the bank problem looming and Mr. Snyder bound to reappear looking for the heiress he had helped escape from the Queen's, it seemed better to move on for a while. She didn't know how the banking people would react, but it was predictable that Mr. Snyder, after a fruitless search in New York for Hiram T. Snelgrove, might not be too friendly.

The Windsor in London wasn't the Queen's in Toronto, but by the time she reached there she was too tired to care or to unpack. She eased her feet gratefully out of her new shoes, hung up her dress carefully, and then fell on the bed and went directly to sleep. It was part of her character to sleep soundly, for Betsy did her dreaming by day.

The serving of breakfast was almost over when she appeared in the dining room the next morning. Not knowing where to sit, she chose a table beside the only other woman eating alone. She was, Betsy noted, rather flashily dressed. Just as Betsy finished ordering, she reached into her beaded reticule and brought out a cigarette case. Betsy had read that there were women who smoked and right away she knew that this must be a woman of ill repute.

Ill or no, she seemed friendly and smiled at Betsy as she took a match from the silver box holder on the table and lit her cigarette.

"New in town?" she asked politely.

Betsy nodded. "New in Canada. I've just come over from England."

"Some difference in Londons, eh?"

They both laughed.

"Are you here on a visit?"

"Not really," said Betsy. "My parents have just died. My mother was run over by a train. Two days later my father was exercising a horse in the rain and got consumption."

"My God!" exclaimed the woman sympathetically, picking delicately at her lower teeth with the end of her match. "So you've come over to find work?"

"Yes, but I'm not sure how to go about looking. Have you any ideas?"

The woman studied Betsy's face. "How old are you?"

"Twenty."

"Twenty! If you're a day over sixteen then I'm a nun! And what are you trained for?"

Betsy shrugged. "What is any woman trained for? I guess I could clerk in a store or something."

"That's damn dull!" the woman exclaimed. "Would you like to do something a little more exciting?"

Betsy nodded eagerly.

"Well, finish your breakfast then and meet me in the lobby. I'll show you how to make a really good living without even getting out of bed!"

Her name was Edna. She lived in a small apartment on Richmond Street, not far from the hotel, and she had a special arrangement with the hotel manager which provided her livelihood. The special arrangement was working so well that she had been looking for someone to join her.

"My God!" she said cheerfully as she led the way into her apartment, "Business is great! The rate the travelling men are passing through town these days I wish I was built like a harmonica! The way it is, if I don't find at least one partner who can help me out, the manager is going to start spreading the business around and I'll lose control of a very good thing."

She stopped in the middle of her parlor, a drab, dark room and stared at Betsy. "You're sure you're a stranger here? No friends?"

Betsy shook her head. "I just came in on the train last night. Haven't even unpacked yet."

"Well, that's good. When I tell you how this game works, I wouldn't want it blabbed all over town. London's a small place. There could be trouble. Up to now, no one has said anything and I'd like to keep it like that."

She glanced around the room and grimaced. "Isn't much, is it? Well, that's the way it's going to stay. Everything I make goes in the bank, except for clothes money. That way, no one is going to start stories about the fancy lady that's living high. Then, someday, I'm just going to up and leave this town, me and my money, and you'll never see me for the dust!" She laughed. "Come on, let me show you the rest. It's even worse, but it's clean. One thing, though, if you come in with me, no callers here. This, bad as it may be, is mine, my place. The landlord lives upstairs. I don't know what he thinks I do for a living and I don't care. But he can never say he saw me bring a man in here. Understand?"

There were two bedrooms off the narrow hall to the kitchen. "That one's yours," she said, pointing into the smaller. Betsy wondered if there'd be room for both herself and her trunk.

"Don't look so down, kid," protested Edna. "I know it's tacky, but remember that if business is good you're not going to spend a lot of time here anyway."

She paused and looked at Betsy standing in the doorway. The girl had class, you could tell that by her clothes. And she had a certain look about her that said she probably was pretty tough inside. Yet . . . "I don't know," Edna said doubtfully,

74

"maybe I'm crazy taking on someone as young as you are, Miss Twenty!" She sighed. "But what the heck, I was only fifteen when I got going. I guess it's better that way, come to think of it. The older you get, the harder the bed. Just don't let the customers know your age, though, eh? Some of them may like the idea but there are others that will shrink right up on you, especially if they have daughters." She reached out and rumpled Betsy's brown hair. "Now come on into the kitchen and sit while I stir up some coffee—it's good too, right from the hotel—and I'll tell you what this is all about."

What it was all about turned into a way of living that Betsy pursued for three years and two months. At first, it was the excitement that held her. The adventure of going to the hotel each night, of meeting men, of learning how to handle them. And there was the money—more than she had ever seen before. Life wasn't all pleasant by any means. Some men drank too much. Some men were cruel. Some even tried to cheat her of her pay. But she didn't want to go back to Eastwood to face her family or, even worse, Tom Wolsey. And the time went by.

After the first year Edna fell in love with a local boy who thought she was a waitress, married him, and moved to Brantford in the predicted cloud of dust. Betsy found two young farm girls to occupy Edna's room and took over the business.

As Emily Heathcliff, friend to all, she made London seem a better place for many a travelling man; and the bank account she had opened the day after she first met Edna and realized that she couldn't go into Edna's business with money pinned to her petticoat grew steadily in size, as did the respect of her bank manager.

He took a great deal of interest in Miss Heathcliff. There was an air of mystery about her that caught his fancy. As a customer she was ideal; she kept putting money in and never taking it out. As a person, she seemed very friendly. She never came into the bank without pausing to chat. Nor were their conversations the frivolous kind he normally had with his other woman customers. Miss Heathcliff obviously didn't know much about banking, but she asked good questions. And even more surprising in a woman, she remembered his answers.

Before too long he became aware of an embarrassing fact: she knew everything he knew. In his defense, let it be pointed out that this branch manager was the product of the Canadian banking tradition, which offered an employee little education beyond the opportunity to study the job immediately above his own. The banks sought out bright boys as clerks, paid them abysmally little, but promised them progress. At the top sat the well-paid assistant general managers and general managers as proof of how worthwhile it could be for those who were diligent and didn't make mistakes. For generations, hundreds of clerks scurried about, obsequious and careful, secure in the belief that by so doing they would rise to the top. Never having compared the staff structure to a pyramid, they missed the point: success was theoretically possible but highly improbable.

Thus Fred Todd at forty-five was manager of a bank, but although he still hoped and although he was a good branch manager, his superiors were not likely to upset things in London by moving him into that glorious echelon already more than adequately filled by relatives and friends of the founding families.

Thus he had only his limited banking background to draw on when Emily, née Betsy, probed for information. He could not take her much beyond debits and credits and his ability to talk about collateral and how far a bank would go in lending money was as restricted as his own lending powers. If someone came to him to borrow more than the amount he was authorized to approve on his own (a maximum of a thousand dollars), he had to forward the application, accompanied by all the pertinent facts, to the head office. There someone he had never met made the decision on a basis that was never revealed to him.

This made Betsy restless. She understood that his lack of knowledge wasn't his fault. But she felt that she had to know more—and his limitations became symbolic of London as a whole. The day came when she realized that she could not stay there any longer.

Her bank account now held enough for her to get by nicely for a while. Perhaps the time had come to do what she had dreamed of doing for so long; moving to the States. The game of entertaining men had become a bore. She had tired of watching them squirm and humble themselves in humbling her, had grown sick of telling them tall tales they had to pretend to believe if they were to get what they wanted. London itself was a nothing place; the poor were very poor and the rich were puffed up with their own importance.

She decided to give her girls the business and to make a trip to Eastwood to see her family, with whom she had had no contact since leaving Tom Wolsey, before striking out for Detroit as a start.

Going home brought many surprises. The greatest was that only her own family recognized her. The three years and a bit had changed her more than she knew. The villagers seldom saw, except at a distance, women who dressed as she dressed, who walked with her pride, or who spoke as precisely and with as much authority as she did.

Her mother cried when she saw her and there was much exclaiming in the vein of "We thought you were dead." Her father looked at her with wise eyes and, she knew, guessed how she had survived.

But the second biggest surprise was to learn that her sister, Alice, had married and moved away. At sixteen, she had been swept off her feet by a man passing through, a Bill York from Cleveland, Ohio. Only a month before Betsy's return she had gone to live with him there.

Cleveland, Ohio! Betsy knew nothing about the place. However, one thing was sure; it would be a better starting point for her new adventure than Detroit, where she knew no one.

On her first night home, she sat down and wrote her sister a letter, congratulating her on her marriage and announcing that she was coming to visit them. On her second night home she decided that she could not stand Eastwood another minute, boarded the train, and left.

Cleveland was better than she had expected. As she emerged from the bustling railway terminal and looked around at the tree-lined streets, she said to herself, "It's quite like Toronto!" and, on the basis of her experience, that was a compliment.

CHAPTER THREE

The flat that her sister and her husband had found was a modest affair at 503 Superior Street. He was a carpenter by trade and Alice had found work as a seamstress. They had just finished buying enough furniture to make the place reasonably comfortable.

When Betsy showed up at the door, Alice was both delighted and dismayed. Betsy's letter had not yet arrived and Alice was all packed and ready to go home to Eastwood for the first visit since her marriage.

The woman at the door was undoubtedly her sister. Yet the change in Betsy during the three years and a bit since Alice had seen her last came as a great surprise. Even though Betsy was not quite eighteen, she had a maturity about her that made her seem years older. Moreover, there was an aura of authority about her as she came in without waiting to be asked that Alice had never seen in the girl whose fantasies had enlivened their childhood hours.

This was, indeed, the sister she loved and about whom she had steadfastly refused to believe the wild rumors that had constantly circulated. Yet, at the same time, here was a stranger whose bearing commanded respect. Alice felt like a housemaid in front of her, and found herself becoming conscious of her worn calico as they talked.

When Bill arrived home for supper, he found his sister-in-law already established in residence. A simple, gentle man who knew nothing of her past, he accepted what he saw; an attractive lady who stood waiting for him to pull back her chair at the table until he got the message. During the meal, she regaled them with witty stories about her experiences as a governess to the Eaton children in Toronto.

When Bill returned from taking Alice to the depot, his sister-in-law had already retired. Which is to say that she had curled up on the parlor sofa under a blanket.

"Are you going to be all right there?" he asked solicitously as he came in and removed his jacket and then his cap.

Betsy rolled over to face him and smiled. "It's not too bad, thank you. If it weren't for my back, it would be perfect."

Bill sat down on the edge of their one stuffed chair. "You have a bad back?"

"Yes," Betsy sighed, "I think it was having to carry those Eaton children around all the time. That's really why I resigned and came here to look for work. I must have a soft bed to be really comfortable."

"Well now," said Bill, "you should have told us! You go in and take our bed and I'll curl up here. I'm used to roughing it."

Betsy sat up slowly, the blanket falling away to reveal her

lace-trimmed nightgown. "I really couldn't do that," she protested. "A big man like you needs his sleep."

Bill shook his head as he got up and held out his hand, "Nonsense! I don't mind a bit, come along."

She extended her hand shyly and allowed him to pull her up. Somehow, the blanket seemed to catch her feet and she stumbled against him. He put his arm around her to keep her from falling and for a moment they were pressed together, her face upturned to his.

"There now," he said, releasing her, "off you go! I'll see you in the morning."

Betsy gave him a calculating glance and shrugged. Alice certainly had a dull husband! She went off to the bedroom and closed the door firmly behind her.

When she came out in the morning, Bill had taken his long wooden tool box and gone to work. His breakfast dishes were piled neatly in the sink and he had set a place for her on the little table in the kitchen. She opened the cupboard. Alice had left some supper foods. There was a meat loaf still in its deep metal plate. Something that looked like a small roast was wrapped in butcher's paper. An unwashed, grimy turnip and a bag of unshelled peas. Nothing that caught your fancy at ten in the morning. She wondered what he had eaten. Then she noticed the pan on the stove. He had pushed it well to the side where it would be away from the heat. In it was bacon and an egg ready to be broken and fried. Betsy poked up the fire and pulled the pan over the lid.

While she waited, she wandered through the flat. What a dump! Her apartment in London had looked like a palace compared to this. Well, she would have to get going and find a place of her own, there were no two ways about it! First, though, she would have to get more money than she had brought with her. But she was not going to dip into her capital, sitting safe and snug in that bank in London. Nobody was going to make her spend that unless she really had to. Besides, she would probably have to go to London to get it, since it wasn't too likely that anyone in Cleveland would accept a check from Emily Heathcliff if Emily Heathcliff couldn't produce any identification. Anyway, Emily belonged to London. Betsy didn't want to bring her—or her occupation—into the Cleveland scene. This was a new story now, and she had always hated having one story overlap with another.

After she had eaten, she piled her dishes on top of Bill's in the sink and got dressed. Alice's clothes weren't very smart and, besides, Alice was taller and thinner than Betsy, so she had to put on a dress of her own. All of the dresses she had packed needed pressing, but she was too eager to get out and explore to wait for the flatiron to heat. She picked the gown that seemed to have travelled best, fluffed up the wings on the shoulders as well as she could, and made do. She would buy new clothes just as soon as she had found a place to live.

She went into the cold November sunshine and blinked at its brightness. After her stay in London, her eyes didn't seem to adjust to daylight as quickly as they used to. As far as Betsy could see in either direction, the buildings all seemed to be the same: dull sets of flats, some of them three stories tall. This wasn't her kind of street.

A surrey was approaching. She stepped out on the road as if to cross to the other side. When the horse was almost beside her, she stumbled and fell. The man in the surrey reined in and jumped down to help her.

She smiled her thanks. "That was very stupid of me!" she exclaimed. "I'm afraid I've turned my ankle. Is there a doctor's house nearby?"

The ride in the surrey to a house with a brass plate on the

door was good for a number of blocks. It took her well out of Alice's district.

"Good morning," she said with dignity to the woman who answered her pull on the brass bell knob, "I am sorry to trouble you but I am looking for accommodation in this area —a little apartment or flat, perhaps. I wondered—the doctor sees so many patients—have you heard of anything that might be available?"

The woman, his wife or housekeeper, thought for a moment. "I only know of one place. It's down the street a piece—149 Garden. A Mrs. Brown—she's a widow—has her lower floor to rent, I hear."

Betsy thanked her and went in search of Mrs. Brown. The minute she saw the house she felt right about it. Like most of the houses in the area, this one had seen better days, but it still retained a lingering dignity. One could invite people there without being too ashamed.

Mrs. Brown was a little sparrow of a woman well past sixty. Yes, she was interested in renting, she said at the door, but— she looked at Betsy with concern—she didn't want any noise in the house, any parties, or any trouble. "Are you married?" she asked.

"No," said Betsy with downcast eyes, "I am a widow."

"Come in, my dear," said Mrs. Brown, "So am I."

The parlor was typically dark, as was the dining room behind it. And the furniture was old and worn. "I've just not had the heart to keep things up since Howard died," the sparrow said with a sigh. "But you could change anything you wanted to. What's your name, my dear?"

"Lydia," said Betsy, choosing one that she had always admired. "Lydia DeVere. My—my late husband was a Frenchman. He died of consumption while visiting the family chateau in the Bois de Boulogne last year. Now I must fend for myself."

"Are you employed?" Mrs. Brown asked, trying not to make it sound like an unpleasant word for a woman to hear.

Madame DeVere shook her head. "I have no talents in the world of men. However," she added, a lovely idea crossing her mind, "I do manage to eke out a living with the one thing I do have to offer."

A line of worry appeared on Mrs. Brown's brow. Lydia saw it and smiled reassuringly. "Two years ago, when my husband and I were travelling in Africa, I met an old witch doctor. From him I learned the secrets of the mind. Before long I discovered that some of his powers had passed over into me. Now, I find that often I can help people by being able to see beyond the present."

"You mean," said Mrs. Brown uneasily, "that you tell fortunes?"

Lydia laughed. "Oh, I'm not a gypsy! No, it is something— well, something larger than that. I can help people with their problems. I can find lost jewels, sometimes. I can reach backward and forward in time. It isn't easy. I suffer a lot in the process. But when people come to me and are helped I feel a great sense of satisfaction. Your husband died of the same thing as mine, didn't he?"

Mrs. Brown looked a little startled at the switch in subjects, but nodded. Lydia sighed. "Why is it that those tall, thin men always seem to go like that?"

"How—did you know Howard?" asked Mrs. Brown.

"No," said Lydia truthfully, "I have just arrived in Cleveland for the first time. But—well, you see how my mind is." She didn't add that the height of the grease stain on the antimacassar of the large chair in the corner of the parlor had given her a clue to Mr. Brown's height. Since the seat cushion didn't look badly sagged, he might have been thin and if he had been his wife's age, consumption as a cause of death was a reasonable bet. She had played this game before with her customers in London. If you were wrong you let it pass. If you were right you took a bow.

She paid Mrs. Brown a small deposit on the rent and left. Madame Lydia DeVere, Clairvoyant, had arrived in Cleveland and was open for business.

First, however, she still had to raise a little capital. She found her way downtown and sought out a company that offered to lend money. She explained her plight simply: the funds from her husband's estate in France had not yet arrived. Until they did she needed enough to live on. What collateral did she have? Betsy thought quickly. "Only my furniture," she said, "it isn't a great deal, but it's all paid for. Would you take a mortgage on that?" They would, but had to see it first. She arranged to meet them at the Yorks' flat the next day and went off to order some business cards.

When Bill York got home that night, he found the house tidy and the roast in the oven. The table was all set and— courtesy of a nearby park—there was even a pitcher of flowers on it. The turnip was a bit lumpy and he had never had peas cooked in their pods before, but all in all, it was a good meal. Afterwards, he settled down quite happily in the parlor to share the *Plain Dealer* which Betsy had brought home with her. Newspapers were a comparative rarity in his life. There seemed to be a great deal happening in the world of which he hadn't been aware.

For her part, Betsy paid scant attention to the wars and rumors of wars. She concentrated on the local news and especially on the reports of social activities. As she read she memorized names. The Rockefellers had returned to their Euclid Avenue home from their summer residence at Forest

85

Hill. Howard M. Hanna's house had been the scene of a party following a race in which a horse, Goldsmith Maid, had broken the world trotting record at, the reporter noted, the advanced age of seventeen. The story was a little confusing for a stranger, but Betsy gathered that all the best families were interested in horses. She made a note to look into the subject. Horses and betting seemed to go hand in hand. And betting could be an interesting thing for a clairvoyant to have some opinions on. There was something in town called the Glenville Track. She decided to go there and see what it was all about.

"Where is it?" she asked Bill. He pulled his mind back from the troubles in France. "Glenville Track? East 88th and St. Clair. Across the street from the old fair grounds. It's only a few blocks. I pass it every morning. The fair used to be quite a thing, but they couldn't make a go of it for some reason, so it closed down about three years ago, I guess. The track is going stronger than ever, though. Last year the guys that own it, them three Rockefeller brothers and Hanna and Brayton and Corning, J. V. Painter, and what's-his-name Everett, they set up what they call the Grand Circuit, so horses come here from way off like Buffalo, Rochester, Utica, and all that, to compete."

"Can anybody go?"

"Well, I guess! When the season is on. If you've got the price of a ticket. Tell you, though, if you want to see some real fun you should go on a Saturday to see what they call the Saturday matinee. It's all amateurs. The young blades, you know? All the toffs, like they say. Each has his private stable there with his name over the door. Every Saturday they come dashing across town in them Brewster wagons of theirs behind big, prancing teams and whirl into the grounds with people shouting and dust flying everywhere. Then they hitch up their racing sulkies and go to it. It's real fun. After, they all go off to a place called The Roadside Club and drink it up and that's the last you see of them. But, like I say, it's fun to watch while it lasts."

"Would you go with me?" asked Betsy.

Bill shook his head. "Can't. My boss'd kill me if I took a Saturday off. He still hasn't gotten over us being allowed to stay home all of Sundays. I went a couple of times before I found work here. But them days is gone now, unless I break an arm and get fired for it!"

"Is it all right for a woman to go alone?"

Bill scratched his short-cropped head. "You got a point. Mostly, it's men as goes. But I have seen women there. Wives, I'd guess, or fancy ladies." He grinned. "Tell you what. You got one of them reticules?" Betsy nodded, "Well, if it's big enough, you could put my Sunday hat in it. Then, when you get inside, you could carry my hat around in your hand like you was waiting for your husband to come back from somewhere. That way, nobody'd bother you."

Betsy smiled. "That's a good idea! But I wouldn't want to take your best hat!"

"Oh, don't worry about that none," said Bill generously, "anything I have is yours!"

The next morning the man from the loan company arrived. He inspected the furniture, gave her the papers to sign, and handed her enough money to keep her going for a month. She wrote a note for Bill, telling him that she had found a place to live and would be in touch. Leaving it on the kitchen table, she carried her bags downstairs and persuaded a passing drayman to drive her to her new home.

The printer had her cards ready. They looked very nice. But how to distribute them? She went into a little tearoom to get warm and think it over. As so often happened with Betsy when she was seeking an answer to a problem, the answer found her. This time it came in the form of an elderly woman seated at the next table. She was bent over her cup, tipping it this way and that and staring into it intently.

"What do they say?" asked Betsy softly. The woman glanced up and smiled gently. "Nothing new, I'm afraid. The same old confused story. I will and I won't, I may and I may not."

Betsy shook her head understandingly. "Tea leaves aren't very reliable. That's why I never use them."

The woman looked interested. "What do you do then? Use cards?"

Betsy's face grew somber and her voice deepened. "No, I turn within myself, to my inner powers. They never fail me. That is why I have been able to help so many, many people." She reached into her purse and drew out one of her new cards.

"Clairvoyant," read the woman aloud.

"That is why," continued Betsy, taking the plunge, "I know what you have gone through since your husband went away." It was a good opening play; the woman was alone and she was wearing a wedding ring. Her husband was probably either on a trip or dead.

"It has been hard," the woman admitted. "If only he could come back just long enough to tell me what to do."

"Perhaps I could help," said Betsy, preparing to leave. "Why don't you come to me? Would eight this evening be a good time?"

The woman nodded. "Yes, yes I'll be there." She hesitated. "I have a friend who has a similar problem. May I bring her with me?"

Betsy smiled understandingly. "Certainly, if you think it will help. But she will have to wait while you and I have our session together. I do not work with groups. That's for charlatans and fakes who need a crowd in order to hide their tricks and devices. I work only with my mind. Reading into some-one else's past is a very private thing. Only you and I will know what has gone on." She patted the woman on the shoulder in a motherly way and left.

As she walked back to her new home, she reviewed what she had taken in. The woman's clothing wasn't high fashion, yet the cloth she had patted was of good quality. No signs of wear. Her purse, open in her lap, had held a long envelope, the sort that might contain a letter from a lawyer. If her husband had been dead a while why would a lawyer be writing her? She said she had a problem. Perhaps it had to do with property; a house that should or should not be sold. It wasn't much to go on, but Betsy had built stories on flimsier foundations before. The second woman would be the real test; it would be necessary to start from nothing with her and feel her way.

She spent the rest of the daylight hours arranging furniture and trying to turn the dull parlor into a place where people would feel relaxed. It wasn't easy. She was sorely tempted to spend some of the mortgage money on new drapes, but she knew herself well enough to know that if she went shopping she wouldn't stop at drapes. Later, she thought, later there will be a man and he will buy the things I need. That is what men are for. Right now, the important thing is to do a good job with these two women so that they will tell their friends about me and send them to me.

As dusk was creeping into the room, Mrs. Brown entered. She glanced about nervously. It was obvious that just the moving of chairs from their familiar spots made her feel that her nest was being disturbed.

"I hope you don't mind the re-arranging I've done," said Betsy.

"Oh no, no," said the little sparrow, "I guess it's really

better this way. What have you done with the damask from the mantelpiece?"

"It's in the table drawer."

"Oh. Oh, that's fine. It's very old, you know. From Damascus. You're having company tonight, I hear."

Betsy looked surprised.

The little woman laughed. "Mrs. Barber—she's a friend of mine—I met her at the butcher's this afternoon and she told me that a friend of hers, Eva Joyce, was going to be taken by another friend to see a mind reader around here this evening. I figured it was you."

Betsy nodded. "I do hope I can help Mrs. Joyce."

"It's not Mrs., it's Miss," said Mrs. Brown with a slight sigh. "Such a pity! A nice woman but she never married. Had a beau, a fine man. Kept company with him twenty-five years, but he couldn't marry her because he had to stay home with his ailing mother. Now he's gone. His heart gave out. And she's left all alone, too old to marry. No family left anymore. She's not poor, Lord knows. The Joyces always had money. But she has nothing to do with her time except feel sorry for herself and visit Tom's grave."

Mrs. Brown's eyes wandered off into middle distance and Betsy knew that she had realized that in describing Miss Joyce's dilemma she had also described her own. These lonely women, what a sad group they were!

"Well!" exclaimed Mrs. Brown, turning off her self pity before it got out of hand. "Have you had tea?"

"No," said Betsy, "I was so busy I forgot."

"Well, then," the frail creature said firmly, "You just follow me upstairs—I've got some nice fresh things from the pastry shop. And you must eat."

It was quite dark when the woman Betsy had met in the tearoom arrived. She and her friend came in apprehensively, obviously not sure what to expect.

As Betsy seated them, she noticed that neither woman volunteered her name. It was as if they were engaged in some nefarious activity where anonymity would be a protection.

"Well," she said cheerfully, "who will be first?"

The two women glanced at each other. "Do we really have to—to do it separately?"

Betsy changed her mind. It might work better the other way now, thanks to Mrs. Brown.

"I have never before evoked the powers in a group," she said solemnly. "But if you really prefer to be together, we can try it. However, you must not be disappointed if it doesn't work." She stood up. "Come," she commanded, "let us go into the unseen world."

She led them out of the parlor and into the dining room. "Sit there," she said, pointing to the old leather-faced chairs at the table. She seated herself between them and reached out a hand to each.

There was one lamp in the room. She had put it on a little table behind where she was sitting, so that now its yellow glow fell on their facees while hers was in shadow.

"Let us reach into the past together," she intoned. "Let us seek guidance from those that are gone." She paused. "Is that you, Tom?" (She felt a rewarding convulsion of the hand on her right.) "Tom, we have some problems. Is there one of us you can help?" Pause. "Eva? Eva—Joy? Eva Joyce? You want to help Eva Joyce? What is it you want to say to Eva Joyce, Tom?"

She waited, listening—and letting the tension in the room build. "Eva is lonely... She needs to be with people more..." Betsy was using a monotone, almost as if she were reading a telegram. "She has a friend who is lonely too... They should work together to fight their loneliness... Her friend owns some property which someone—a lawyer—is trying to get her to sell... She should not sell... She and Eva should live together there and make the lower floor into a tearoom. . . Eva has the family money. . . Her friend has the property. . . It will work well." Betsy paused for breath.

"Is there no message for me?" asked the woman on her left. Betsy tilted her head and listened. No voices came. "Not tonight," she said quietly. "Not tonight, my dear. Somewhere, somewhere a long, long way off there is a voice trying to be heard. It's coming closer. A man's voice. But it will not make it tonight. I'm sorry."

She released their hands and stood up. "That is as far as we can go this evening," she said. "As I suspected, it does not work well when there is a group. I hope you will let me try again—with each of you alone."

"Oh, we will! We will!" exclaimed Eva, wiping her eyes with a square of lace. "If only you knew what you have done for me!"

Betsy had a pretty good idea.

"Helena," said Eva, leading the way out of the dining room into the hall, "come home with me; we must have a talk." She turned back to Betsy. "Is there some way we—we can reward you for your help?"

The great clairvoyant, having thought that one out in advance, raised her hand in a gesture that indicated disdain for the things of this world. "You will find a silver salver on the hall stand," she said with great dignity. She bowed her head, went back into the dining room, and closed the door. When she knew that they had left, she dashed out to check the tray. There were two dollars on it.

Two dollars! A week's wages for some! She had expected them to leave a twenty-five-cent piece each, perhaps a half dollar. This was wonderful!

She grabbed the money and whirled into a little dance around the living room. And they would come again! And they would send their friends! And she would be rich! And life was wonderful!

If only there were someone she could tell! She stopped dancing. That was the sad part of it all. Life was exciting. A great and wonderful adventure. Sometimes, like now, the excitement boiled so high it wanted to overflow. And she had no one with whom to share it.

It would be nice if Alice and Mary and Emily were here now, sitting around her on the floor as they used to do, listening with their mouths open and their eyes shining. How they would love the story!

But no. Alice was married to that grubby man and Mary and Emily—well, they looked at her differently now. She had become a stranger to them. When she had gone home from London they had hardly spoken to her, treating her almost the way they treated a person who had come to the door to ask directions.

She shrugged. There was no need to ask directions from anyone anymore. She could find her own way. Who needed friends anyhow? As Cassie Cushing used to say of men, if you got too friendly, they only used you anyway.

Betsy turned out the lamps and went into the little bedroom off the dining room. After she had undressed, she put the two dollars on the bureau—thinking back whimsically to her livelihood in London—and went to bed with Lydia DeVere.

CHAPTER FOUR

R ising early was not one of Betsy's attributes. Of all the maxims she had heard in her childhood, the one she had rejected most heartily was "Early to bed and early to rise makes a man healthy, wealthy, and wise." She had observed that early to bed and early to rise produced some pretty dull and certainly not wealthy farmers.

It was easy to sleep in at Mrs. Brown's. Apparently, her landlady shared her inclination. The house rarely had its curtains parted until noon.

On her second day Betsy found the Cleveland library. The mere presence of so many books excited her. At first she flitted like a butterfly from topic to topic, pausing here, darting there, reading a bit of this book and then a bit of that. After the first few days, though, a more productive pattern began to emerge.

As soon as she arrived in the reading room she would go to the newspapers and, after glancing at what was happening in the world, turn to the stories on social activities in Cleveland. She noted who was entertaining, who had become betrothed to whom and, because it might be useful in her new business, who had died.

Then she would pick a book from the stacks the way a less precocious girl not yet eighteen might choose a sweet. With it, she would return to the reading room and sit absorbed until the coming darkness made seeing the print too difficult.

Nor were these novels that she read. History fascinated her, but then so did chemistry and medicine and philosophy. She was hungry for knowledge and retained a surprisingly large amount of what the books told her. Had Cassie Cushing, the school teacher, been able to observe, she would have sighed for the girl who hadn't gone to college.

This way of investing her afternoons went on for over a month without interruption.

Eva Joyce came back one evening for more advice from Tom. Her friend, Helena, came and was able to get confirmation from her William that she and Eva should set up shop together. These satisfied customers sent some friends. The dollars began to appear on the silver plate with increasing frequency. And the more she worked at it, the better Betsy became at telling her customers what they, without realizing it, had already told her.

It was a good life in its way, marred only by the growing difficulty she was having with her hearing. It was vitally important to the clairvoyant's success that she catch asides between customers or little half-murmured exclamations of reaction as she communed with the dear departed. During her last winter in London she had developed an ear infection. Now, in the early damp spring, it had come back. The pain in her ears was now more intense than before, but the loss of acuity bothered her more than the pain.

At Mrs. Brown's suggestion, she went to see a doctor. It was the same one at whose house she had called when seeking a place to live. Number 3, Garden Street was a cut above Mrs. Brown's house in size and appearance. The waiting room was well appointed and so, she noted when she met him, was the doctor.

Wallace S. Springsteen was a doubly dedicated man. Not only was he committed to his profession, he was also driven by a desire to rise in the world socially. Unfortunately, whatever his capabilities as a man of medicine, he was singularly ill-equipped to achieve the latter goal. Born to parents of modest means, his professional manner of quiet competence deserted him completely when he was confronted by anyone whose apparent wealth or position was greater than his own. He who could amputate a limb with deftness would stutter over the weather in a social scene in which he felt inferior.

It was not strange, therefore, that when Madame DeVere came to him, haughty and wrapped in new furs, his first reaction was one of panic. This was not lessened when her history of previous problems with her ears included references to the dampness of French chateaux and the searing heat on African safaris.

He pulled at his long, thin chin and tried to look wise, but he was less conscious of her illness than of cutting an awkward figure before this polished lady.

Betsy saw his discomfort and, with her sure instinct for opportunities, began to play on it. Her ear infection required a series of treatments. For each treatment he gave her, the shy doctor got one in return as Betsy worked in under his guard and finally got him, not without effort, to the point where he felt safe enough to touch her elsewhere than in the area of her ears.

In retrospect, she might have been better advised not to have distracted him from curing her; while the pain went away, her hearing did not improve and gradually deteriorated during the rest of her life.

However, by November of 1882, Betsy had so cured *him* that he was able to propose marriage. On the 21st, they appeared before Justice of the Peace Babcock and were wed. There was enough news value in the event—a bachelor doctor marrying a clairvoyant—for the Cleveland *Plain Dealer* to run a story on it. With the story appeared a photo of the smiling couple taken as they emerged from Babcock's office.

For years, Alice York and her husband had had no word from Betsy. All efforts to trace her had failed. And then, suddenly, there she was in the newspaper!

Madame DeVere indeed! Alice and Bill marched right over to 3 Garden Street and demanded to see her. The new Mrs. Springsteen, said the maid, was not receiving. Her husband, alas, was not in a position to invoke that social rebuff; such was the price of having a waiting room.

If the shy doctor was shocked by the story Alice and Bill told him of how his new wife—really, apparently a sister to this Mrs. York—had mortgaged their furniture and run off, he was more than shocked when their call was followed by visitations from all sorts of tradesmen to whom she owed money. All of them, including the Yorks, seemed to expect him to pay her bills.

He didn't try to total up all of her indebtedness; whatever the sum was it was more than he possessed. In any case, he was too upset to care. Nor was Betsy's winsome admission that she had been a naughty girl sufficient excuse.

In the hope that it might indeed be, as she alleged, a plot to disparage her devised by a jealous sister, Doctor Springsteen engaged detectives. Within a few days they returned with their report. Not only had she not been Madame Lydia De-Vere, she also had not been, they said, exactly faithful to him during their period of courtship.

On the eleventh day of their marriage, Betsy was ejected from the house. And on the twelfth day, the doctor filed for divorce on the grounds of infidelity.

Alice, Bill, and the creditors were chagrined. The doctor refused to help them in any way. Betsy, shocked at the cruel treatment she had received, decided to leave Cleveland for a while.

She took the train to Erie, Pennsylvania and—feeling very depressed and alone in the world—checked into the Reed House as Mrs. Mazie Brown. She explained to the management that she was recently widowed and wanted to be alone with her sorrow.

Since she was obviously a woman of quality, the manager went out of his way to make her comfortable. Had he known that, in her eagerness to quit Cleveland she had arrived without funds, he might have been a little more cautious. As it was, he and his wife made a practice of calling on her from time to time in the hope that they could cheer her up.

After several weeks had gone by and the manager, for all his admiration of the brave little woman, was beginning to wish that she would pay something towards her account, Mazie was suddenly taken ill. The very night that he, having discussed the matter with his wife, had decided to present Mazie with her bill to date, a doctor had to be summoned.

The poor woman had taken to her bed with a violent cough and was spitting blood. Unaware that as a child Betsy had discovered that she could produce blood by sucking her gums, the manager viewed this symptom of hemorrhaging with some alarm. It was now not only a matter of being nice to the poor young widow, it was also a question of the hotel's best interests. Given a choice, hotel managers prefer not to have their guests die on the premises.

When Mazie rolled her eyes and pleaded to be sent home to Cleveland to die, the manager was quick to call a hansom and escort her to the train. He and his wife helped her to board, made her as comfortable as they could, and paid her fare.

A couple of weeks later they received the following unsigned letter:

"Mazie has passed peacefully away, putting her full trust in God at 2 o'clock on March 27. Poor Mazie's remains were taken to her native home in Canada for internment, and were followed to their last resting place by a large and sorrowing concourse of friends."

Betsy found Cleveland still a little warm that winter and decided not to take up residence again for a while. Hotel life had been so pleasant and inexpensive in Erie that she went to Buffalo and registered at the best inn there.

At this point in her career, we see the first inkling of the greatness to come. Previously, she had thought in hundreds. Perhaps marriage is, as some aver, a broadening experience. At any rate, at a time when others might have felt it prudent to tighten the belt a notch, Betsy simply added a zero to the money she had in mind.

To Dr. Springsteen's annoyance, he received a letter from a lawyer in Buffalo. It demanded, on behalf of the lawyer's client, Mrs. Lydia Springsteen, the sum of six thousand dollars which, the lawyer claimed, he had promised to pay Mrs. Springsteen in return for her having agreed to a separation.

Now, since Betsy had had no choice in the matter (the separation had had physical overtones: she had found herself on

Day Eleven standing on the wrong side of the Springsteen front door), she did not expect her Buffalo lawyer to receive a check by return mail.

However, she was starting to think big. And the whole matter of choosing a lawyer, meeting with him, and waiting for Springsteen's reply helped pass the time pleasantly—and the manager of the hotel, shocked by the callous treatment of such a refined lady, was more than helpful and patient as he joined her in waiting for the money.

When, at last, he could no longer afford to go without payment, Betsy had the good taste to sense his dilemma. To save him the embarrassment of having to confront her, she quietly moved out one night through the back door and checked into another hotel under another name.

This process went on until May, with Betsy moving in a circuit around Cleveland, waiting until she felt it was safe to return.

Early in May, she made a quick trip to London and Eastwood. In London she withdrew her funds from the bank. In Eastwood she stayed with her parents—but only between one train and the next, for there she learned from letters Alice had written home that Doctor Springsteen had finally given in to the importuning of her creditors and, in some cases, the pressure of their lawyers and settled all her debts.

Leaving her family marvelling at the goodness of the Providence that had rescued Betsy from the hands of so evil a man ("Imagine him forcing his wife to do those things!"), she headed directly for her chosen Mecca.

Within a day there was in residence and ready for business at 359 Superior Street, Cleveland, an excellent and perceptive clairvoyant by the name of Madame La Rose.

However, Madame did not stay long at that address; 359 was too close to 503 where Alice and Bill still lived. It wasn't that they themselves caused her any trouble. They simply ignored her. But rumors travelled up the street to her landlady's ears and she was asked politely but firmly to move on. This she did, to the home of a Mrs. Sweeney at 66 Prospect Street. There, whatever her background, she was welcome and settled in to await customers and build her future.

As the weeks passed, she found herself wishing more and more for another Dr. Springsteen. Money was not coming in as quickly for Madame La Rose as it had for Madame De-Vere, and her savings from London were being spent at a faster rate than she liked. They would not have been spent at all, had it not been for her recent bad experience with tradesmen, in consequence of which she felt it behooved her to pay cash for a while.

She also lived in fear that some inveterate pursuer of conversations with the dead would show up and cry—loudly enough for at least Mrs. Sweeney to hear—"But aren't you that Madame DeVere who took poor Dr. Springsteen?"

Thus it was that when John R. Scott, farmer, showed up on her doorstep and said he wanted to get his late wife's advice about buying a second farm, she took him in gladly and soon had his mind off the past.

Big John, it turned out, lived down in the Mahoning Valley. He didn't get to town much—which sounded a little discouraging. But when he explained that that was because he had such a big farm to operate, Betsy could see that it would be a problem for him.

Big John, for all his success as a farmer, was not a very sophisticated man. When the truth finally dawned on him—that this little, plump but attractive French lady actually thought he was handsome—he was so overcome that he would have followed her anywhere. When he confessed this to her as he was about to leave one morning, she pointed out that it wasn't right for him to give up so much because of her. Love meant sharing. If he wanted, she would marry him and go with him to his farm.

However, there was one thing. She told him of her unhappy experience with the cruel doctor who had robbed her of her inheritance and then thrown her out in the snow. Even now, lawyers were suing him to recapture her fortune for her. Until the case was settled, she was penniless.

"It is not," she explained gently, holding one of John's thorny hands as they sat side by side on Mrs. Sweeney's settee, "not that I don't trust you, Johnee, but I have come to the point where I just can't make myself trust any man. In any case, I couldn't marry you until the divorce from that monster comes through."

"Oh, Marie!" exclaimed her swain, using the name he had learned to love since meeting her. "What can I do, what can I say?"

"Well," said Betsy slowly, "maybe it would help if we had a contract. I know that sounds terribly businesslike. But if you would sign a paper promising never to touch my inheritance once I get it back, I think I could overcome this foolish fear I seem to have."

"Anything! Anything at all!" the fervent farmer cried, crushing her to him.

That very day they went to see a lawyer. The resulting document simply said that if and when John R. Scott married Marie La Rose Springsteen there would be no dowry and that he waived all rights to any property that she might then or subsequently possess. Somehow, in the discussion of the agreement an element of confusion seemed to creep in, perhaps because John's mind was more on the possession of his bride than on possessions. In any case, the marriage contract also stated that if at any time for any reason Marie should leave him, then John would automatically forfeit to her all that he possessed.

In October, the courts granted Doctor Springsteen his divorce and so Lydia DeVere, Betsy Bigley, and Marie La Rose were all free to marry. (Mazie, of course, was dead, the Elizabeth Cunard who once visited Toronto was just a memory, and Emily Heathcliff had vanished with her bank account.)

Marie and John R. were wed in Youngstown in a ceremony which, at the bride's request, was informal and quiet. But there was nothing quiet about their arrival at Big John's farm in Trumbull County.

He, proud man, had done a lot of boasting to his friends between his trips to Cleveland. The coming of a bride was news but even bigger news was that she was French. ("Well," he explained, "not really French, but she was married to a Frenchman once. And she sort of talks Frenchy.")

The reception the new couple received when they arrived at the farm made 1883 a year to remember. People had come for miles. The yard was full of buggies and the big old wooden farmhouse was full of people. Fortunately for the bride, they had all brought food, as was the custom. The women had gone through the house cleaning and dusting and (as Marie discovered later when she was able to inspect the garbage heap back of the barn) had tactfully removed the little evidences of Big John's earlier marriage.

Tommy O'Flynn, the fiddler, was there and after they had eaten a space was cleared in the front yard for dancing. Even the bride, who was ignorant of such things, was spun and tossed through squares and reels until she thought she was going to be ill. It was such a wild, gay evening that some of the guests didn't leave until ten.

At last, however, the newlyweds were alone and Marie

had a chance to look at the furniture. It wasn't worth much.

"Well," she thought as the eager bridegroom blew out the lamp beside the high-backed bed, "maybe the land is worth something."

The next day Big John took her around the property. And then he drove her over to meet the people on the adjacent farm which he was thinking of buying. Marie could see immediately that he was right. It should be bought. The owners were getting old and were anxious to sell and move into a village. Big John could remove his separating fence and have enough land to more than double his grazing area. That would mean twice as many cattle fattening for market and twice as much income.

It would also mean, John explained on the way back, that he would have to mortgage his own farm in order to buy and stock the other. That didn't appeal to Marie.

"But Johnee!" she exclaimed, hooking her arm in his as he drove, "there is no need for that! I have a little money, let me pay!"

John gave the horse a snap of the reins on its back. "No. Any money you got is yours. We made that paper. Anyway, a man don't take money from a woman."

She hugged herself to him. "But I am your wife! Everything you've got is mine—and so everything I've got should be yours. It's only fair."

It took a bit more arguing and persuasion, for John was a man of standards. In the end, however, she was able to persuade him and the last of her London money found its way with a little help into his account in Youngstown and thence to the owners of the farm next door and to cattle dealers.

As Marie had suspected, John was a good farmer but he didn't know much about handling money. Now that she had a stake in the operation, she began to help him in that area.

At first he resisted, for his standards said that women should be homemakers, not moneymakers. Marie soon changed that by pointing out that it was silly and costly for him to take time off from farming to go to the bank.

Soon it was she who made the trips to Youngstown. Not long after, they changed the bank account into her name so that she could withdraw as well as deposit.

Because of the smallness of Youngstown and the limited range of things in its stores, it wasn't hard for Betsy to restrain her normal tendency to buy whatever struck her fancy. Perhaps for this reason in this period of her life the pendulum of proclivity swung the other way. She found pleasure in not spending, in making do wherever possible. In consequence, as the months went by and more and more cattle went plodding down the dusty road to the slaughterhouse, the bank account began to grow at a very satisfying rate. And John, who had so reluctantly let her handle their money, began to boast to his friends about what a wonderful little manager she was.

In addition, for a woman raised abroad and accustomed to the finer things in life, Marie showed an amazing ability to adjust to the rigors of farm life. "Why," said John one day to his friend Herb Schneider who ran the store at the crossroads, "you'd think she'd been born on a farm! And her English is getting better too. There's hardly a day now when you hear any French accent at all!"

If Marie was content with her new life, the time came when Betsy wasn't. The novelty of being on a farm three times the size of anything near Eastwood, of being able to help its income grow, of having her husband in a constant state of amazement and admiration was wonderful—but it wasn't enough. To Betsy, the real thing was somewhere else.

It was as though she had a sense of destiny. After four

years of marriage, at a time of life when most women would have thanked God for a good man and a good home (for girls married early then and over twenty was not a very marketable vintage), Betsy grew restless. She had the marriage contract safely hidden away. She knew she could leave at any time and take all Big John's assets with her. What she sought was a purpose and a direction, a challenge.

For a time she thought that perhaps she had found it in the possibilities presented by a contact she had made in the course of doing business in Youngstown. Mr. Richard Brown of the feed firm of Brown, Bonnell and Company was an attractive older man who found in his only lady customer growing reasons to see his wife with critical eyes.

He also found it difficult to keep pace with the escalating intimacy of his relationship with Betsy. Youngstown was not yet big enough for the meetings that began in his office to move across the street to the privacy of a hotel room without the clerk talking. Betsy, accustomed to the anonymity that a city the size of Cleveland could provide, was irked by her new friend's timidity. He would not even walk down the street with her.

Finally, his attitude became the catalyst she needed. She saw him as narrow, straight-laced, unimaginative and just plain dull.

For a long time, going to Youngstown had been her outlet, her way of escaping from the tedium of farm life. Now she saw Youngstown as simply a condensed version of that life. The people were just the same except that they lived on streets.

Thus Betsy told Richard "the truth"; Big John was cruel to her and she was going to leave him lest she suffer actual bodily harm. This was a side of Big John that Richard, who had known him for years, would have found hard to accept had he stopped to think about it. Unfortunately, her confession of marital conflict so filled him with fear that she was planning to move to Youngstown that he didn't question her story in his anxiety to accede to her request, when it came, to help her escape to Cleveland.

When she declared that she wanted to leave that very day, he was glad to help. He took her straightway to his own lawyer to discuss the divorce she wanted. While they conferred, Richard went to the depot and bought her ticket. And, in one great gesture of bravery, he even accompanied her to the station and stayed there on the platform until the train was safely in motion.

Only after she was well on her way and Richard had returned to his office did he learn from his somewhat shaken lawyer that Mrs. Scott, since she wanted a quick divorce, had insisted that the lawyer act not for herself but for Big John, and had left with him a sworn statement confessing herself guilty of adultery on many and specific occasions with Mr. Richard Brown, respected head of Brown, Bonnell and Company.

"But you can't do this!" Richard exclaimed, jumping up from his swivel chair. "You're my lawyer, not hers!"

The lawyer frowned. "You brought her to me, Richard. I assumed, in fact, dammit she told me, that you wanted it this way! In any case," he added ruefully, "I think we'd better proceed. She has kept a copy of her statement and she proposes to send it to the paper here if there is any delay. If we go to court, we may be able to keep it reasonably quiet, provided Mr. Scott cooperates, of course. But if we don't, you'll be the biggest news since the Flood."

A few days later, the lawyer got a letter from Betsy telling him that correspondence on the matter they had discussed could reach her care of a Mrs. Hoover on Cleveland's Euclid Avenue.

"Please note," the letter concluded, "that I am using my

middle name as a means of sheltering myself from the unpleasant past. Hence, I should be addressed not as Marie, but
as Lydia, Mrs. Lydia Scott."

The lawyer wondered how a farmer's wife could afford
a Euclid Avenue address. When he checked discreetly at the
bank, his friend the manager made it clear. Mrs. Scott's
newly-chosen bank in Cleveland had just presented him with
a check which cleared out Big John's account.

Betsy soon found that she had taken more with her from
the Mahoning Valley than she had realized. Shortly after
she moved in as a roomer with the widowed Mrs. Hoover, her
mornings became unpleasant. Although her experience by
now was very broad, it did not include what she now needed
to know; how to prepare for motherhood.

Needless to say, pregnancy hadn't been on her agenda.
When a discreet visit to a doctor removed her last hope that
the symptoms might be those of some less encumbering
malaise, she had a meeting with herself and decided to make
the best of it. Thank goodness she had escaped from John
Scott in time! No child of hers would ever be born on a farm!

It would be far better for him or her (or them, for all Betsy
knew) to be able to claim Euclid Avenue as a birthplace.
And while the old Judge Griswold place that Mrs. Hoover
had rented at 122 was not to be compared in size or condition
with the Hannas' or the Rockefellers', it did have the magic
address.

No one really knew why Mrs. Hoover had chosen it. Perhaps it was because the house seemed as empty and gray as
her life had been since her husband had died.

In any case, she had rented it without telling her children
in Buffalo or even consulting her lawyer—who certainly
would have tried to discourage her, not only because it was
obviously too big for a woman over sixty to manage without a

staff of servants, but also because it was far beyond her means.

She had been in the house only a few months when she began to realize her error. Once she had paid the monthly rent there wasn't enough money left from her late husband's few investments to pay for maids or other normal amenities.

Thus Mrs. Hoover had placed in *The Plain Dealer* the advertisement for a room for rent which Betsy had seen when she arrived from Youngstown.

Bored and lonely, Mrs. Hoover welcomed Betsy into her heart as well as her home. She had been a little timid about having a stranger in her house, but when a young woman of obvious breeding appeared at the door—not some flighty thing but a woman who, it transpired, had also been married and was now alone—despite her financial need she would have given her a room just to have her stay.

In this climate of being wanted and, as Betsy could see, needed, it was easy for the mother-to-be to confess, with due evidence of distress, her unfortunate condition.

"Oh, you poor dear!" exclaimed Mrs. Hoover as they sat over tea in the parlor. "And what of the father?"

"Alas," said Betsy (she loved 'alas'), "I am afraid I cannot expect much help from him."

"He's dead?" asked Mrs. Hoover sympathetically, pushing her tiny glasses back up their well-worn path on her nose.

"It's worse than that," sighed Betsy. "When I first came to Cleveland alone, I was a widow. I was very, well, innocent. You know?" Mrs. Hoover nodded. Innocence was a handicap she understood.

"So I looked for advice," Betsy continued. "Through a friend of my father I was directed to a lawyer here who said he would help me." She smiled bitterly. "He helped me indeed!" Her small hands touched her abdomen lightly. "How unsuspecting I was when he invited me to dinner at his flat!"

"But you should go to him and tell him what has happened!" Mrs. Hoover protested, giving her glasses a reproving jab. "No matter what kind of villain he is, he can't deny his own child!"

Betsy shook her head sadly, "It's not that easy, I'm afraid. He is not only a lawyer, but a very prominent man. I do not feel that I should speak his name, even to you. But dared I do so you would recognize it instantly for he is, well, let us say he is very high up in the Democratic party. So you see, a man in his position could not afford to have a thing like this become public."

"All the more reason why he should want to help, at least financially!" exclaimed Mrs. Hoover indignantly.

Betsy looked shocked. "I could not ask for money on that basis," she protested. "That would be blackmail! In any case," she added quietly, "money is not a problem for me—at least for the present. My last husband, I mean my late husband, provided for me rather well—and there is more to come when the estate is settled."

Mrs. Hoover ran her knobby hands through her fading brown hair, "Well then," she concluded, "there is nothing for it but to have the child and make the best of it, is there?"

"Do you mind?" asked Betsy. "Having a baby in the house, I mean. I'll move if you wish."

"Mind! Of course not!" Mrs. Hoover smiled. "It will be wonderful! Just like having one of my own all over again! Mine have grown up and married. They live up in Buffalo and I seldom see them any more. Not that I mind, you know, they have to lead their own lives now. But sometimes it would be nice . . . Why don't we start preparing a room right now! Maybe the one next to yours?"

Betsy raised a hand in protest, "You're very kind, but I

think the baby and I will have to share. I can't afford it, really..."

"Nonsense!" laughed Mrs. Hoover, "the room is standing empty and I'm certainly not seeking another boarder, so how could I charge you for it?"

It was the kind of logic that Betsy loved to encounter in others. Even though the unblessed event was months away, she and Mrs. Hoover went shopping for a cradle that very afternoon.

The months that followed were a lull in life for Betsy. As the child within her grew large, she tended more and more to stay indoors, helping Mrs. Hoover with the seemingly endless task of keeping the big home presentable against that day when, the poor lady was convinced, her children and her children's children would arrive to visit Grandma. What time she had to herself, Betsy spent reading.

The late judge had left to his tenant a great array of books on many topics, far beyond her limited interests. To Betsy, however, exploring his shelves was like playing with diamonds.

Dickens was there, of course, with all his power to caricature. And Ruskin, saying of Dickens, "the things he tells us are always true." (Betsy, taking Ruskin's statement at face value, formed some opinions on life in England which were, if not accurate, at least the source of some interesting conversations later, when she encountered people from that country.)

John Stuart Mill gave her, through his *Principles of Political Economy*, some sense of how the governing of the world was or should be ordered. She memorized a few of his thoughts for later use.

She skimmed through the judge's well-marked translations of Plato and Xenophon, Cicero and Horace. Where his pencil had pressed especially hard, she paused and thought and remembered. She encountered Dante's avaricious Geryon and saw but rejected the simile of how, like her, he had gathered air with his claws of greed.

Letters arrived from Youngstown occasionally. The lawyer was pursuing his assignment though, she could tell, not with relish. To her relief, there was silence from Big John. She assumed that he accepted the truth of her sworn statement and wanted to be rid of such a hussy at any price.

Finally, the day arrived when the doctor had to come and help her give birth. It was a boy. She named him Emil because it sounded French and distinguished.

As soon as the baby was old enough to travel, Betsy bundled him up and boarded the train for Woodstock. It was time to resume her pursuit of that undefined but exciting goal that she believed awaited her in life. For the present, Emil was too young to pursue it with her. His day would come. Meantime, he would stay with her parents.

They met Betsy at the station and took the baby. She did not even go home with them to Eastwood, but caught the next train back. The divorce had come through and her lawyer was coming to Cleveland with the final papers for her to sign.

To her surprise, when she arrived at Euclid Avenue she found Mrs. Hoover packing.

"I've decided to go to Buffalo," she explained. "Actually, I've wanted to for some time. I miss the children so! I waited until your baby came, thinking that having it around would help. But now that he's gone, well, there's nothing to hold me here." She pushed up her glasses and peered around with distaste. "It was foolish of me to take on this monster in the first place. I'm sorry, Lydia. Will you be able to find another home?"

"Not as nice as this," said Betsy frankly. "You've been very good to me."

As it turned out, Mrs. Hoover's decision to leave the house on Euclid did not inconvenience Betsy. When Betsy's lawyer arrived that afternoon, he told the former Mrs. Scott that her recent husband's mood had changed once he realized that not only her virtue but also his property was at stake in the divorce. By the terms of the marriage contract they had signed, Betsy was now the owner of his land, his house, and his chattels.

"I'm sure he'll make a very good tenant," said Betsy calmly.

"He may," admitted the lawyer, "but I suggest you move to a new address. I hear he's threatened to come to Cleveland and find you. If he does, I assume he will act violently."

"Alas," said Betsy, "the poor misguided man! Well, I suppose that to spare us both I should leave Cleveland for a while! If you would be kind enough to act as my agent, collect the rent when it falls due, and see that it is deposited here to my account, I would appreciate it."

"Where will you go?"

"I don't know," said Betsy sadly. "Perhaps I shall travel on the continent. I will write to you on my return."

That night she packed her few things and, having said a fond good-bye to Mrs. Hoover, took the train to Toledo. She stayed overnight at a modest hotel and in the morning went hunting for a home.

After some searching, she found a small apartment in an old house on Broadway at the corner of Clayton.

Once again, the proprietor was a woman, but of a different sort from the gentle Mrs. Hoover. This buxom lady had interests of her own. They came and went at all hours. Her philosophy on tenants seemed to be, "The less they bother me, the better I like it."

"Would you mind if I hung out a little sign?" asked Betsy.

"Tell me what kind of sign," the landlady demanded with some suspicion, not being one who liked to advertise.

"Oh, just my name—Madame Lydia DeVere—and what I do; I'm a clairvoyant."

"A clairvoyant! One of them crystal ball types? Well, I guess—so long's it's not a big sign. Like a doctor's shingle, eh? No bigger."

Betsy managed to move her bags from the hotel without disturbing the management and moved in on Broadway. The house was nothing like the old Griswold place, neither so grand nor so well located. However, the rooms were bright, the bed was soft and, surrounded by a strange new city, Betsy felt good there.

Building a clientele was easier now, for she had had experience. This time she did not waste her energy on getting into conversations with aging widows in tearooms. With thirty looming ahead, she felt a sense of urgency which translated itself into concentrating on men. She went directly to the nearest bank and, in the course of opening an account, charmed the manager into becoming her business development counsellor.

Before long she had developed a small but enthusiastic group of middle-aged businessmen who found it within the scope of conscience to visit a clairvoyant—for this, while some might question its value, was a socially acceptable practice. The fact that matters of the mind were not the only ones explored at Betsy's was never mentioned outside her home. Nor was anyone likely to raise an eyebrow if she visited a client at his place of business or greeted him on the street. The arrival of Emil had served to increase her tendency to plumpness and the years of warring with the world were giving her once-gentle features a sternness which only her coterie knew could soften in the night.

As always, she kept looking for the right man; the man who could lift her to the heights where she was convinced she belonged. Each of her patrons knew—and believed that he alone knew—her secret, the romantic story of her past. And whether to one she was the daughter of a famous British general, to another the widow of an earl, or even, in one case, the niece of President Ulysses S. Grant, each believed her, admired her bravery in the face of adversity, and did what he could to help.

It would, in fact, have been better for Betsy if she had tried even harder for the heights through marriage. Other routes to wealth were fraught with danger, especially for one who, with the waning of what youthful beauty had been hers, was getting a little over-anxious and inclined to press her luck.

She did not realize this, however, the day she devised a new plan for increasing her income by making use of the obvious effect she was having on one Joe Lamb.

CHAPTER FIVE

J oe Lamb's name seems well suited to the role Betsy devised for him. Joe was a man of unquestionable honesty and integrity. He had a wife and five children. The Lamb family lived modestly, for Joe's salary as an express company clerk was only about a thousand dollars a year. Nonetheless, Joe had managed by the age of forty-eight to save a little money.

As Joe occasionally called on a friend who roomed in the same house as Betsy, he happened to meet her in the hall several times. After his friend moved, he might have forgotten these casual encounters entirely, had Betsy not appeared at the express company office one day in late September and asked him to send a parcel of money to Cleveland for her.

He recognized her as soon as she came up to the counter and was flattered to note that she knew his name. (One presumes that Betsy had done a little research before Joe's roomer friend moved on.)

After he had taken care of her parcel, they chatted pleasantly for a moment, and she invited him to call on her.

It took Joe a week to get up his courage. It was not in his nature to seek adventures, but the promise in Betsy's dark eyes kept haunting him. On his way home from work on Friday night, he finally gave in to the stirring in his groin and went to see her.

The meeting was not entirely successful. His conscience was so filled with guilt that he felt genuinely ill. And to make him even less appealing, Betsy noted that he was suffering from what she hoped was only a temporary tendency to have a running nose. As the little man stood before her, twisting his cap and inquiring repeatedly as to whether she was sure her parcel had arrived safely in Cleveland (for he obviously felt that his visit had to be justified in some way), she actually felt sorry for him. A lamb indeed!

Realizing that if she rushed things she would frighten him off, Betsy took it easy. They sat down in her room and chatted a while about the weather and a steam-driven carriage someone was said to have invented and how long he had been at the express company and what a pity it was that Queen Victoria had never seen Toledo in the spring and how Betsy's uncle had always wanted to bring her but the Queen had never had time.

The mention of time brought Joe to his feet. A picture of his waiting wife and children filled his mind and he stumbled to the door—but not before, between sniffs, he had promised to return as soon as he was feeling better.

The cold in his nose disappeared before long, but the guilt

in his heart lingered on for a while. He knew that he had really done nothing wrong. What haunted him was that he wanted to. It was a case of mental adultery. As a disease, it took two weeks to run its course and then turned into acute lust. He appeared at Betsy's door free of sniffles and panting for action.

Unfortunately, his friendly clairvoyant already had a customer and he could not be admitted. Betsy came to the door to apologize.

"But do come again, Mr. Lamb," she urged. "I must be away this week. My sister, Mrs. Brown in Cleveland, is ill. When I return I do want to see you." She looked deep into his eyes and saw the fire smoldering. "Mr. Lamb," she murmured, "if you could help me..."

"Just tell me how!" exclaimed Joe, willing to take on dragons.

"Well, I have done rather well this year but, as you know, I have had to send money to Cleveland to help pay my sister's medical bills. And now, just when I should be taking the train there, I find myself temporarily short of money. I know this is imposing on our slight acquaintanceship, but I was wondering if you could let me have twenty dollars to see me through? You would, of course, be repaid as soon as I get back."

Joe was embarrassed. It almost seemed a demonstration of her mind-reading powers. Twenty dollars was exactly how much he had in his pocket, no more and no less, for it was payday and that was how much he earned per week. When he got home there would be food to buy and rent to pay and dear knows what else. On his way to Madame DeVere's he had also thought that it might be a good idea to buy his wife a little present.

"Well," he stammered, "I—I . . ." He lowered his eyes.

Betsy aged about thirty

The dining room,
the house on
Euclid Avenue

Betsy in her late forties

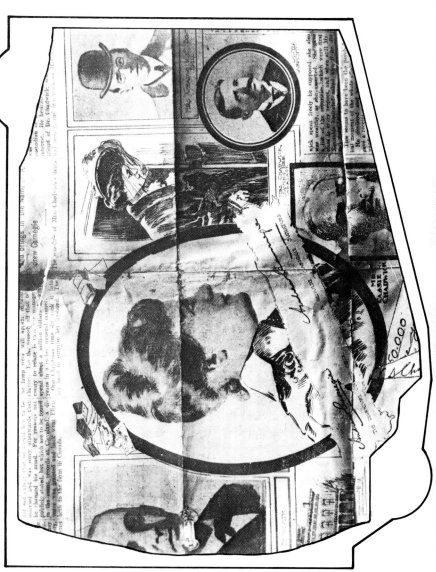

Press clippings from the
time of the trial

Dr. Leroy Chadwick

The Chadwick house on
Euclid Avenue

The drawing room

Betsy/Cassie in 1904

Courtesy of *Plain Dealer*

Courtesy of *Plain Dealer*

Courtesy of *Plain Dealer*

Betsy in her prime

On this forged note the daughter of an Ontario section boss swung her biggest single hoax. She had hinted that she was the illegitimate daughter of Carnegie, that she was heir to millions in bonds.

One of Betsy's greatest hoaxes

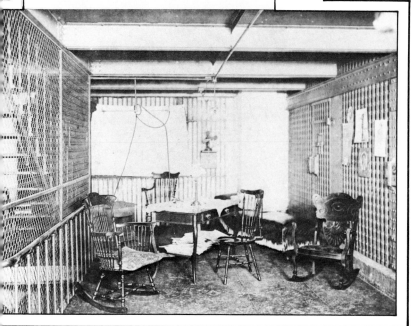

$5,000,000   New York, May 20 1904

Fifteen Months after date I promise to pay to the order of C. L. Chadwick

Five Million Dollars

at No. 1824 Euclid Ave., Cleveland, Ohio.

Value received

No.   Due   Andrew Carnegie

Andrew Carnegie
Andrew Carnegie
Andrew Carnegie

Andrew Carnegie
Cassie L. Chadwick

TO WHOM IT MAY CONCERN:—

We take sincere pleasure in testifying to the competency and efficiency of Prof. H. D. Gould, both as a hand-writing expert and microscopist. In our practice we have had several occasions to retain hand-writing experts, some of them having a national reputation. We have no hesitancy in saying that Prof. Gould is the superior of any with whom we have been heretofore associated.

He was retained by us recently in a case which required expert knowledge, not only as to hand-writing, but also with reference to microscopical analysis of dynamite, nitro-glycerine and other substances. His services in all these lines were of the very highest character and resulted in sustaining our theory of the case, and securing the acquittal of our client on a most serious charge.

Very sincerely,

Akron, Ohio, Jan. 17, 1906.   YOUNG & WANAMAKER.

Two of Betsy's forgeries

Betsy's prison cell

Betsy in jail

3 6 6 8 0

ELIZABETH BIGLEY
WIFE OF
L. S. CHADWICK M. D.
1859—1907

The grave in
Woodstock, Ontario

"Yes, Joe, what is it?" asked Betsy, moving closer. She wore perfume. Joe's wife took her Saturday night bath faithfully, but this was Friday.

"I—twenty is all I earn," he blurted out frankly. "I—I could let you have five of it."

"Oh, thank you!" exclaimed Betsy. "I know that will help. And the fact that it came from you will make spending it all the more meaningful."

Joe took out one of the four fives in his pay envelope and put it into her little white hand. In return he got a kiss. Not one of your brazen hussy kisses on the lips, but a chaste little brushing of his cheek. By today's standards, it wasn't much for five dollars. But to Joe it was a tingling, exciting experience. In twenty-odd years of marriage, this was the first time he had been touched by a woman other than his good, drab wife. This kiss, this fleeting contact, had cost him twenty-five percent of his income, but what it did for his manhood was worth every cent. He left the house on Broadway whistling, head up and shoulders back. The only thing he regretted was that he couldn't tell his wife why he felt so wonderful.

The week that Betsy was away (or, for we must keep our perspective, told Joe that she was going to be away) dragged slowly for him. Finally it was Friday and Joe was back on the doorstep.

This time he got in. Mrs. Brown in Cleveland was worse, he learned, and his new love was obviously worried. Her own health was being affected to the point where she had had to stop seeing clients.

The kiss on the cheek the week before became a fervent clinch as Joe put his arms around her in a gesture of sympathy and felt her respond to his embrace. He gave her ten dollars toward her sister's medicine.

The following Friday he found her in tears. Her sister

had died, leaving two children. Since there was no longer a Mr. Brown to help, the full load of the funeral costs fell on Joe's love's shoulders. She had to find fifty dollars right away.

"I wish I could give you all you need," said Joe miserably as he sat on the side of her bed holding her hand. "But I have only the little savings I have put by for our—my old age. Would twenty help?"

Lydia DeVere smiled up bravely at him from her pillow and nodded. "Why are you so kind to me?" she whispered.

When Joe came back next week he found her much improved. The funeral in Cleveland was over and clairvoyancy was once again being practiced. Betsy assured him that once her health was fully recovered she would be making two or three hundred a month. There would be no problem about her paying back Joe's money soon.

The weeks of cold December went by with Joe growing more and more enamored. He began dropping in at noon twice a week. Just before Christmas, she gave him back every cent he had advanced.

And then came the good news! She explained it to him happily as they lay curled up together before the fire. Some years before, in a moment of girlish impulsiveness, she had married a wealthy Britisher who lived near Manchester, England. There was a great age difference between them, but he had been very kind to her. "I felt I was his daughter," she confided shyly. Unfortunately, just a month after their marriage, his horse had taken fright and tossed him to his death in the River Styx, which ran through his property. This was why she was in Toledo; she had come to America to forget.

Now she had just received word from his lawyers that the estate had been settled. She would from now on have an annual income of a thousand dollars.

To Joe, who had to work the full fifty-two weeks a year

for that amount, it seemed a windfall indeed. Further, the money changed their relationship in a subtle way. They were now not only lovers, but almost partners.

He still marvelled at what a woman of her breeding and background saw in him. His honesty extended even to his self appraisal. He knew that he was a timid, unlearned clerk. Yet she liked him and found happiness in him. He was so proud of this that he would have done anything for her.

It did not seem strange to Joe—in fact, it seemed only reasonable—that while she awaited her first check from England, Lydia turned to him for money to see her through.

From Joe she obtained first a loan for $100 which he borrowed from the Ketcham National Bank. Then she needed $200 and then $200 more—and his note grew. By the end of February, as no money had arrived from England and Lydia was, as she herself confessed, seriously in need of medical treatment, Joe got a friend of his, J. J. Mattocks, to co-sign a new note for $300.

This brought his total contributions to date to the thousand dollar level. Since Joe was very concerned about his debts, being the kind of man who heretofore had prided himself on owing no man, Lydia insisted, over his protests, that he accept her personal note for the full amount, payable one year after date. Joe then gave her a note for $273, payable three months after date, so that she could send it to her physician in Cleveland, to whom she owed that amount.

Unfortunately, when this latter note came due, it showed up at the Second National Bank in Toledo with evidence on it indicating that she—or possibly the doctor in Cleveland—had bought with it a sealskin coat.

Even though it appears that this transaction did start Joe thinking a little, he could not make an issue of it, for just as he was opening the subject on the afternoon he found out, she burst into tears and told him that that very morning her Toledo doctor had examined her and announced that her operation could no longer be postponed. It would cost a great deal of money and she simply did not know what to do.

Joe was immediately, as always, filled with sympathy. "Don't worry, Lydia," he assured her, stroking the white hand that rested between his legs, "we'll find a way. If only your check from England would arrive we could use it to pay what I owe now and start afresh."

"I know," Lydia nodded, "I can't think what's keeping them. I've written and written."

"Don't you have anything left at all? Is there nothing?"

"Well, not exactly. I do have a note a friend of my father sent me, but it's not payable for a long time. Do you suppose someone would lend us money on it in the meantime?"

She fished a piece of paper out of her purse on the night table and handed it to him. Written in a strange, back-slanted script was a promise to pay her one thousand dollars twenty months after May 1st. The signature was that of someone named Fabin.

When Joe took it to the Ketcham Bank they let him have $400 on it, which he hurried to give her. Thereupon she persuaded him to find and pay a Mr. Hattey to whom she owed money and to redeem the jewellery she had pawned, "so that I can face my operation with a clear conscience and know that, if anything happens, you will at least have my jewellery to sell."

About this time, her illness progressed to the point where, as she explained with tears, she could not see Joe as often as before. Through that long, hot summer he had to go weeks without being admitted to her room.

A strange young lady, tall and thin with wild black hair and a silk patch over one eye, had appeared on the scene.

Lydia introduced her as Madame La Frette, a friend from her Paris days who, having heard of her illness, had crossed the ocean to be at her side. Madame La Frette was also, it evolved, a clairvoyant and was helping to keep the business going until Lydia could get back on her feet.

"Doctor Chillip says she is very good for me," Lydia whispered. Joe could not help but agree, for she obviously had the ability to make Lydia laugh, something that he, very concerned about their debts, could no longer do. He often heard them laughing together after he left the sickroom.

From Madame La Frette, who now was the one to turn him from the front door when Lydia could not see him, Joe learned in August that Lydia had had her operation and that it had been successful (although to his dying day he never knew what had been taken out, rearranged, or installed; it was obviously something feminine and unmentionable). Now the long period of recuperation was in progress—and, with it, the long struggle to pay for whatever it was that had been done.

Using his last thing of value, Joe pledged the diamond stickpin his father had given him and sent the money in through the forbidding, one-eyed guardian.

Lydia was so touched that she had him admitted. Their reunion, despite her whispered cautions about straining her incision, was very satisfying. Joe felt very much a man again, which was just as well, because when he came back to see her the following week he found himself being really tested by Fate.

Lydia's doctor had decided that the operation was not successful and would have to be repeated. This time, he had said, a specialist would be required and that meant that she would have to go to Philadelphia.

"But we can't afford it!" exclaimed Joe. "Live or die, there's no more ways I can raise money! As it is, I daren't go near the bank."

Lydia looked at him sadly for a moment, then a brave smile lit her face. "Now, now, my darling," she whispered. "You mustn't think of taking this extra burden on yourself. I'll manage somehow."

The next time Joe came to call, Madame La Frette told him Lydia had already gone to Philadelphia, but she had left him her love and would send him word as soon as she returned.

Six long weeks went by with no message for Joe as to whether she was alive or dead. And then one day Madame La Frette came to his office to say that Lydia was back and would like to see him.

He practically ran all the way to Broadway and Clayton. And there she was! No longer bed-ridden, but up and about and looking as desirable as the first time he had met her! Apparently the specialist in Philadelphia had been a great man indeed, for in this enthusiastic and prolonged reunion, Joe could find no evidence of an incision at all. They had a very happy time, full of laughter and mutual gestures of affection.

The topic of money didn't come up even once until he was leaving. Then Lydia did admit shyly at the door that she had no money for food or rent. Normally, Joe would have given her five or ten dollars. But on that day he happened to have in his pocket the sum of $300. It wasn't his; he was holding it for friends as the stake in an election bet. Without a thought for the consequences, he pulled out the wad and pressed it into her hand. When Lydia saw how much it was (which did not take long, for whatever her other shortcomings, she could count rapidly), she urged him to come back in so that she could thank him properly.

However, he was by then hopelessly late for dinner and felt he needed what energy he had left for the fray on the home front.

When the election was over, Joe was in an awkward situation; the winner of the election bet wanted his money. Later he testified, "I have always felt very guilty over this, for it was the first time that I had compromised myself. I was, to say the least, wild with worry. I did not know what to do or what to say."

He finally got out of it temporarily by getting his friends to accept his note.

When he related this to Lydia she waved away the situation as being petty, for she had just received word from good old England that an uncle had died and left her $5,000 in cash. As soon as she had it, she would pay Joe back all of his money and his problems would be over.

There was, of course, one small delay in the way; she had to go to England and be identified in order to collect.

For a moment Joe had that sinking feeling. Lydia laughed at the expression on his face and kissed him reassuringly, "Don't worry!" she exclaimed. "I'm going to see my Uncle Brown in Cleveland. I know he'll let me have the price of the trip, so long as I promise to pay him back."

When Lydia returned from Cleveland, it was with a long face. Uncle Brown had been most unreasonable. The money in England would just have to sit there until she could find the boat fare to go get it.

Joe was equally discouraged—and beginning to be a little frightened. Creditors were pressing him to pay off notes and if he couldn't find $1,200 right away, it was certain that he would have to go to jail.

"Well, my darling," sighed Lydia, "I got you into this so I guess it's up to me to get you out. Tell you what we'll do:

you give me two notes, one for $700 and the other for $500. I figure by now Uncle Brown is feeling a little bad about letting me down. I'll go back over to Cleveland and get him to give me cash for the notes and then you'll be all set."

Joe, who was beginning to get a little confused over how many notes were coming and going, heard only the word "cash" and reached for his pen.

Alas, Lydia had apparently underestimated Uncle Brown's mood. She came back from Cleveland in a dark state of mind and empty-handed. "I was so angry," she told Joe, her eyes flashing, "I tore up your notes and flung them in his face!"

Even in his own dark moment of despair Joe could not help but admire her spirit. This admiration faded somewhat in a couple of weeks when Sipe and Sigler, a firm of jewellers, contacted him for payment on one of the notes which had been used for the purchase of jewellery, and a few days later when a man who said he was a friend of Madame DeVere asked for what was due on the other note which he had accepted in exchange for money to help the poor and ailing clairvoyant.

Not unnaturally, Joe went to Lydia to protest. And, for the first time, he went with ire. Brushing aside Madame La Frette, he charged into Lydia's room.

Caught *en deshabille*, her modesty showed itself in a hurried attempt to tidy up the bed which was, indeed, in a state of wild confusion, looking for all the world as if somebody had left it in a great hurry.

Joe was in no mood to wait for the completion of her housekeeping. He spun her about to face him.

"My notes," he began, "those notes you said you tore up . . ."

"Have come due," Lydia completed for him. "That's the trouble with notes. People always end up wanting the money. Well, thank goodness, it's all over."

126

"What's all over?" Joe demanded, his hand still on her shoulder. Lydia lifted the gripping fingers free and pressed them to her lips.

"You poor man! I have given you a hard time, haven't I? Well, we've come to the end of that, Joe Lamb. The lawyers say I can tell you now." She pushed him back gently into a chair and stood over him.

"Tell me what?" Joe asked, conscious that in order to look her in the eyes his line of sight included her wonderful, soft breasts barely covered by her lace night attire.

"Tell you what?" echoed Lydia, running fingers through his thinning hair. "Why, what all this sad charade has been about." She moved closer, so that to see her eyes now Joe had to tip back his head. It was an uncomfortable position yet he felt compelled to keep looking into those dark wells and to have her gaze fixed on him. Her fingers in his hair began to stroke him gently but firmly in a slow and steady rhythm.

"Do you love me, Joe?" she whispered.

He blinked to show his assent.

"Will you always love me?"

He blinked again.

"People who love each other believe each other, no matter what. That's right, isn't it Joe?"

Her voice was low and dusky. The fingers in his hair kept stroking.

"Once upon a time, Joe, there was a little girl who was very frightened. You know what it's like to be alone and frightened, don't you?"

Joe wanted to nod but couldn't. He could only close and open his eyelids slowly to show that he understood.

"Well this little girl—her name was Florida—lived in a big, big house over in Cleveland. Her daddy was a very rich man named Mr. Blythe. He owned a lot of property, whole city blocks of it. And he was always very busy buying and selling things. He loved his little daughter very much but he could not spend much time with her.

"And that was unfortunate, Joe, because her mother was a cruel woman. Perhaps she was jealous of the love Mr. Blythe had for their daughter. In any case, she used to beat the little girl and do horrible things to her.

"It finally got to the point where the girl could not stand it anymore and ran away from home. The mother searched high and low for her and even hired detectives to try to find her and drag her back. But the girl had changed her name and, even though she was never far from Cleveland and saw her father from time to time, she was never caught.

"Unfortunately, because her wicked mother suspected that her husband knew where Florida was, he could not even give the poor girl money for fear of his wife finding out. So the girl had to fend for herself and make a living as best she could.

"Well, that's almost the end of the story, Joe, except for the part I couldn't tell you or anyone before. Not long ago the wicked mother died. For a brief time, it looked as though Florida could at last give up the life she had been living and return home. But unfortunately, before she could, her father met with a terrible accident and died. His will left everything —all his wealth and property—to Florida G. Blythe. But who was she? the executors asked. It had been years since the Blythe girl left home. She would be a grown woman now. They did not know where to look until, one day, someone walked into the office of one of the lawyers involved and said that she was Florida."

Joe's eyes had closed now. But he was listening, taking in every word of the story the deep, quiet voice was unfolding.

128

"Naturally, they were suspicious," Lydia went on, "the woman could well have been an imposter. As you may have guessed, I was that woman, Joe. And you have no idea what it is like to try to prove who you really are after years of pretending to be someone else. Even Uncle Richard found it hard to help."

"Uncle Richard?" Joe muttered.

"Uncle Richard Brown. I used to have two uncles named Richard, so we always called this one Uncle Brown. Anyway, for years Daddy and I had used Uncle Brown's office as our secret meeting place. Yet that very secrecy was now an obstacle, for we had made a practice of coming and going separately and unobserved. And even though Uncle Brown knew what had been going on, he could not actually swear that he had ever seen us together.

"When I turned to him in desperation, he did hire a lawyer for me at his own expense. And a detective, too. It was the latter who finally solved my problem. He found the doctor who had brought me into the world. A very old man now, nonetheless he remembered a birthmark I have. That little star on my hip? Well, it was because he had never heard of a child born with a star on it before that he could recall even now. That last time I went to Cleveland—the time I took your notes with me—we had a court hearing. It was very embarrassing, for I had to expose myself to the judge and those lawyers. But when they heard the old doctor testify and then saw the star for themselves, they were convinced.

"I'm sorry about the notes, Joe. I did intend to tear them up, but I got confused with all this going on. And, anyway, it doesn't matter now, for soon I will have my inheritance and you and I will be so rich that none of this will matter."

Lydia stopped stroking his hair and bent to kiss him. At the touch of her lips, Joe's eyes opened and he smiled. Taking his hand and resting it on her breast, Lydia asked, "Do you feel better—now that you understand?"

Joe nodded. There were questions he wanted to ask, but they seemed somehow very unimportant. He drew Lydia—Florida—to him and buried his head contentedly in her cleavage.

A few days later when he came to see her again, he found her in high spirits. "The money is starting to come through!" she exclaimed happily as soon as they were alone. "Uncle Brown is handling the whole thing. But until that's done, Uncle Brown is giving me money of his own so that I'll have some to live on. Here's his first check!" Lydia handed a slip of paper to Joe. It was a check for $5,000.

"But this is drawn on a Youngstown bank," Joe noted.

"It's what?"

"I said it's drawn on a Youngstown bank."

"Oh that! Well," exclaimed Lydia, "that's where Uncle Brown lives now. He still has an office in Cleveland but his iron manufacturing business is really in Youngstown and he has moved there to be closer to his work. Are you on your way back to your office?" Joe nodded. "Well, then, why don't you take this first one—there'll be more—and put it in your own account? You can use it to pay some of those dreadful notes!"

"But I couldn't take the whole thing!" Joe protested.

"Nonsense! Remember, I'm going to be wealthy now. And the first thing we should do is clear the debts from the past. Of course, if you want to bring me five hundred or so when you come tomorrow, I could use it."

Joe did as he was bid. A few days later, he was given another large check from Uncle Brown. And then another. Soon he had the past debts all cleared away and was depositing checks in Lydia's own account at the bank.

Everything was wonderful now. His sense of having come out of a dark woods into sunlight was even more intensified when Lydia gave him a note for $25,000, signed by Richard Brown. "He wants me to have a real advance on my money, as proof of his integrity," she explained. "I suppose I shouldn't take it but he has been so kind lately I don't want to hurt his feelings. Would you mind taking it to the bank for me and getting them to hold it? They'll want to charge for that, of course, the usual way they discount notes for cash. But if you see the President, Mr. Nearing, I'm sure he won't be hard on us."

As it turned out, Lydia's assessment of Mr. Nearing's attitude was not very accurate. Some of the recent checks Joe had taken in for deposit had found their way back from the bank in Youngstown where, it seemed, there was no account on which they could be drawn, nor, so far as that particular Youngstown bank's records showed, any Mr. Richard Brown. If there was no Mr. Brown, asked Mr. Nearing of Joe, how then could he sign a note for $25,000?

That seemed to be a reasonable question. Joe wished Lydia were with him to answer it. "Well," he said at last, "I guess I'll have to go back to the person who gave that to me and find out where the mistake is." He reached to take the note from Nearing.

"I'm afraid it's not that simple, Mr. Lamb," said the manager, slipping the note into the center drawer of his desk. "You see, if the signature on this is a forgery then so, perhaps, are the signatures on the checks. And since you presented them and obtained money for them, I hope you won't be offended if I point out that you may have been guilty of a felony." He raised his hands when he saw the stricken look on Joe's face. "Oh, I know, Mr. Lamb! You've been a steady customer here for years. I do not doubt for a moment your own honesty—or, at least," he amended, "the honesty of your intentions. But, unfortunately, the law doesn't always see things the same way as people do. As a banker, I have no course open but to turn this matter over to the police. As a man, I can only say I hope that it will be cleared up without your good reputation being tarnished." He offered his hand. "Whatever you do, whatever steps you take on your own to straighten this out, I do hope you won't do anything foolish. You know, I should really call the police right now, and I would if you were a stranger. But I'm assuming that you won't leave town and will be available for questioning if and when they need you."

When Joe reported back to Lydia (no matter how he tried, he could not make himself call her "Florida") she immediately flew into a rage. As he testified later, "She was terrible mad, called me everything, and said I was the biggest fool in existence. This was the first time I ever saw her get beyond the control of her temper."

The cause of her anger seemed to be that he had let Nearing keep the note. She brushed aside the talk of forgery and cried that Uncle Brown would be ruined if it got out that a note of his had been questioned.

"But where is Uncle Brown?" Joe demanded. "The bank in Youngstown has never heard of him!"

"That is nonsense," replied Lydia coldly. "He is known all over Youngstown and Cleveland. Some young clerk is just being stupid."

"I hope so," said Joe, "because I am very sure the police will be here before long to question us. Uncle Brown had better appear on the scene soon."

Lydia shook her head. "It mustn't be like that. He has to protect himself and his family. Look Joe, you go get a lawyer. Any lawyer, so long as he's smart, and bring him back here.

We'll work out a story with him that will satisfy the police and that will be the end of it."

"Another story, Lydia?" asked Joe sadly. "What do I need a story for? I've done nothing that needs a story to cover it, unless, perhaps, there's more truth to what Mr. Nearing suspects than you've told me, in which case I've been a fool and a dupe."

At this point Madame La Frette knocked on the bedroom door and came in, closing it behind her.

"There are two detectives in the parlor say they want to see you," she whispered to Lydia.

"Now see what you've done!" exclaimed Lydia crossly to Joe. "Well, let's go face them. Perhaps they're just on a fishing trip."

It was no fishing trip. They had warrants.

Under the date of Wednesday, January 15, 1890, two entries appear in the turnkey's blotter at the old Toledo police station:

"Lydia DeVere, forgery, arrested by Detectives Manley and Brown, Clayton St. and Broadway, clairvoyant, born Canada, age 33, 6 p.m. Bound over, grand jury, county jail transfer, Jan. 25, 1890."

"Joe Lamb, forgery, Manley and Brown, express clerk, England, 6 p.m. Bound over—bail bond by clerk."

Joe was out on bail by seven and home with his family. Lydia sat in jail for ten days before they came up for trial. Of the two locations, probably the dingy cell was the pleasanter, for with the trial pending and the likelihood of conviction great, Joe had to tell his wife all that had happened. Well, almost all. It is reasonably certain that he did not dwell on how personal his relationship with Lydia had been. The evidence for this is that when the trial began, Mrs. Lamb and their children were in the audience and remained there until it was over.

What might have been just another case of forgers brought to justice was given extra attention by the press because of the pleas involved.

Joe's lawyer was a man called Irvin Belford. His defence was that Joe had been an innocent dupe. And then, as he recalled later, he had a lucky break. "A few days before I made the final plea for him, I read that a prominent French physician claimed much for hypnotism in the treatment of cases." He seized on this and succeeded in impressing the jury with the thought that his client had been so unbelievably gullible because the clairvoyant had mesmerized him. It was an ingenious idea and gave the jury the opportunity to excuse the actions of their local citizen.

Nor was the proposition wholly without a base in fact. As Belford later told a reporter, "I have talked with prominent men and attorneys here, and they say that while they were in her presence they could not resist feeling uneasy, for she had some way of securing their assent to almost anything she proposed. The ease with which she got hold of prominent men was a wonder. I remember one old man, very wealthy, who gave $3,000 and a diamond stud worth $300 without any security, not even a promissory note. She told him she needed these before she could have any control over the spirits that she was to call in to aid in some matter in which he was interested."

Hypnotized or just plain stupid, Joe Lamb was acquitted and left the court a free man. Penniless and broken in spirit, he ended his days peddling paint from door to door and died at an early age.

Lydia's defence also featured an interesting approach. Her attorney, Judge Ritchey, simply maintained that since the charges hinged on her having posed as Florida G. Blythe, there could have been no fraud because of the fact that such a person did not exist; she was a myth.

It was a daring move. By focussing the jury's attention on the question of whether it was bad to pretend to be someone who didn't really exist, he made good yards around some very damning testimony.

For example, there *was* a Richard Brown. Not, by any means, Lydia's uncle, but real nonetheless. And the evidence that came out on her handling of him was pretty explicit. Apparently, she had gone to his home in Youngstown (how or why she chose him was not revealed) and said that she was sick and in distress. He gave her enough money to enable her to return to Toledo.

Immediately on her arrival there she mailed him back the money, as she had promised she would. He did not acknowledge getting the money, so she wrote again to inquire whether it had arrived safely. To this second letter, he sent a short reply.

The signature on his letter became a very useful tool. So good were the copies made of it that they fooled the First National Bank, the Northern National, and the Merchants National. Even Brown himself said after the trial that under ordinary circumstances he would have believed that he had written the signatures himself.

The best Judge Ritchey could do with this was to show that while his client certainly had seen Richard Brown, accepted his help, corresponded with him and, indeed, passed checks and notes bearing copies of his signature, there was no proof that she herself had made those copies. He alleged that a friend of hers whose writing was similar to Brown's was the real forger. Since the friend went unidentified and no one had actually seen Lydia sign anything, his rebuttal planted a reasonable doubt in the jury's mind.

The prosecutor, J. H. Southard (later to become a Congressman) seemed to be losing his case. Lydia had been charged with forgery and fraud. Forgeries there had been, but he had failed to prove that she had committed them. Fraud hinged on her having said she was Florida G. Blythe, heiress. Her counsel said that Florida was an invention.

And then, on the last day of the trial, there was a scene worthy of a television court-room drama. Southard was offering his testimony in rebuttal and had just finished interrogating a witness, when one of his clerks gave him a signal.

Abruptly ending his cross-examination, he waved the witness from the stand and, in a voice that commanded the full attention of judge and jury, cried, "Please call Florida G. Blythe!"

Out of the ante-room walked a well-dressed woman of middle age. Sworn in, she stated that she was, indeed, Mrs. Florida G. Blythe of Cleveland.

It was obvious to everyone watching that Lydia was as surprised as anyone there. Judge Ritchey was thunderstruck.

Southard questioned Mrs. Blythe with great courtesy, establishing her position in Cleveland society and her integrity. He then asked her, "Have you ever met or had any dealings with the defendant, Madame Lydia DeVere?"

Mrs. Blythe shook her head. "Until your representative approached me and asked me to testify, I had never heard of such a person."

That was that. Southard summed up his case. The jury retired briefly. After it emerged with its verdict, Madame Lydia DeVere was sentenced to nine years and six months of hard labor in the penitentiary at Columbus.

INTERMISSION

(During the Intermission
Lydia DeVere sews shirts.

Length of Intermission:
Three years and six months.)

CHAPTER SIX

The parole was finally signed by Governor William McKinley. Madame Lydia DeVere was free, and Betsy Bigley went home to Eastwood.

The only times that Madame DeVere appeared again were when she had to report to the parole board. When these reports were no longer required, neither was she.

About a year after Betsy's release from the penitentiary, a Mrs. C. L. Hoover took up residence at 166 Franklin Avenue in Cleveland. Living with her were her mother, sister, and five-year-old son. This was in 1894. The fact that Madame DeVere had to check in with the parole people periodically until mid-1897 did not seem to prevent Mrs. Hoover from living, as the press later commented, with "conspicuous extravagance."

The source of her income during this period never came out at the time of her final trial. A side of Madame DeVere (to which poor Joe Lamb was never exposed) suggests a probable explanation. During the day and a half he was examined and cross-examined at the Toledo hearings, Joe consistently depicted her as a lonely woman, usually in bed or an invalid's chair, who had turned to him as her only source of help.

He was, indeed, an innocent.

As Captain O'Dwyer, the head of the Toledo police department said, "He would no more think of going into a saloon than a minister of the gospel." If he had not been so free from guile he might have had a shorter and less disastrous experience. What he didn't seem to realize was that the reason he so often found Lydia in bed of an afternoon was that she was tired from the night before.

Had he been an evening caller instead of a day caller, he would have been part of a quite different scene. To quote from the Toledo press:

> Madame for the most part looked for higher game. Bankers, businessmen, professional men of high repute, foregathered at the apartment on Broadway near Clayton where she held her court and there was high revel by night and well into the morning. Men jollied each other over their beer about the banquets and social sessions with "the DeVere" and her comely associates, for the Madame, a prepossessing woman herself, usually had an attractive friend to assist at the entertainments.

Back in Cleveland, with her mother, sister, and Emil living with her, Betsy could not organize any "high revel by night" in the house she had rented on Franklin Avenue. Yet the life style she sought required contact with men of affluence. For this reason she reverted to the role she had learned at such a young age in London. The Madame of Toledo became a madam in a Cleveland brothel.

No doubt Betsy saw this business as providing only a temporary solution to the need for money. After the years in the penitentiary spent planning the future and dreaming dreams, it is unlikely that Betsy could have been happy for long among the sordid realities of a house of pleasure.

As it turned out, her employment as a madam was short indeed. One night not long after she had gone to work as an overseer of sin, a customer arrived who was to change her whole life and open the way to everything she had always wanted.

The moment that Carrie, the maid, told her who was waiting downstairs, she felt a surge of excitement. Dr. Leroy S. Chadwick. Euclid Avenue. Money. When Carrie asked whom she should send down to take him on, Betsy told her that she would see him herself.

It was a bit of a risk; he might have known of her in the past. But, she thought, he would not remember. Almost thirteen years had passed since her divorce from Dr. Spring-steen, and—what with her marriage to that dreary farmer, Scott, her adventures in Toledo, her three and a half years in that awful penitentiary before Governor McKinley came to his senses and paroled her—her recent exposure to people in Cleveland, and especially to people who lived in Dr. Chadwick's Cleveland, had been very slight.

Even as she thought, she took off the rather gaudy gown she usually wore during working hours, splashed water on her face from the basin in the corner of the room, and took out of the cupboard the one simple, plain dress she had. It had to be a fast change. She could have used more time. But opportunities like this would not wait for everything to be right. She had learned long since that sometimes you had to act fast, improvising as you went.

As she went slowly down the stairs, she became a dignified and innocent widow left penniless by her husband's unexpected demise, a woman of good family come on hard times. She sensed that Dr. Chadwick was pacing up and down and so she paused before entering to wait until he was facing the curtains which closed the arch. Then she parted them slowly and went in wearing the smile of a hostess welcoming a stranger who had come for tea.

Betsy found facing her a pleasant-looking man of about her own age. (At that time she was almost forty but made it a point not to show it!) He had a rather sensitive face, small head, long neck, black hair above a rather high forehead, and a full but well-trimmed mustache partially hiding with its drooping ends what she suspected might be an encouragingly weak chin. As a fortune teller and clairvoyant, Betsy had learned to make quick assessments of people's characters. In this case, she liked what she saw.

He came toward her respectfully and she asked him to be seated. It was immediately obvious that this was no regular visitor to a brothel. He was quite lacking in self-confidence. Betsy sensed right away that his need was more for companionship than sexual satisfaction.

As they chatted quietly about generalities, he gradually began to relax. She led him to talk about his home and soon gathered the real motive for his visit, the need to escape a wifeless house filled with memories and ailing relatives. From that it was easy to bridge the gap between them by telling him of her own unfortunate loss. As he missed his daughter, Mary, who was away at boarding school, so, Betsy admitted, she missed her little Emil who was of necessity living with his grandparents on their Canadian estate.

"However," she sighed, "I don't think it would be right for me to have him live here, do you?" Dr. Chadwick was aghast at the thought. "I mean," she went on in an innocent way, "this is my first day as manageress of this home for girls so I don't know anything about it yet. But it seems to me that a little boy might suffer from a plethora of female attention."

"Your first day?" Dr. Chadwick asked.

"Yes. I'm afraid I simply have to work to make ends meet—and, like so many women in my position, I do not have any special training. Fortunately, a lawyer friend of my husband heard of this opening and was able to arrange for me to come here. So far, it seems rather pleasant. The girls come and go a lot, and I must say some of them seem rather, what shall I say, of coarse breeding? But I hope that I will be able to be a good influence on them. There is, I must confess, a lot to do. Apparently, the previous manageress thought nothing of letting them entertain men visitors right here in the parlor at any time! I have told them gentlemen may call only at proper hours and only when I can be present to chaperone. It is so easy for a girl alone in a big city like this to get a bad reputation, isn't it?"

"But Mrs. Hoover!" he protested, "Surely, madam, you are not trying to say that you are unaware of—I mean, you do know where you are?"

"Of course I do!" Betsy replied sadly. "I realize that these homes for girls are not what we would wish. But it is far better for them to live in a place like this than perhaps fall inadvertently into the trap that waits on every street corner. If you, Dr. Chadwick, were of lowly means and had a daughter, wouldn't you prefer her living here rather than running the risk that she might—how shall I put it—find herself involved in a house of ill repute?"

Dr. Chadwick looked at her with what seemed to be pure astonishment. Betsy asked him what was the matter.

"But madam," he burst out, "this *is* a house of ill repute! One of the best known in all of Cleveland!"

The force of his statement brought Betsy to her feet. "You— you must be mistaken, sir!" she exclaimed.

He shook his head sadly. "No, I am sorry to say, it is the truth."

By this time in her life, Betsy was so accustomed to immersing herself in her roles that any extremes of emotion called for came naturally and with no apparent guile. As his revelation sank in, she actually felt faint and tottered. He came to her in compassion and put his arm around her shoulder. Betsy leaned her head against his rather narrow chest. A tear appeared on her cheek.

"Whatever shall I do?" she whispered. "My God, what would my father think if he could see me now? Oh, I am so ashamed! I've been so stupid and so blind!"

"Now, now," he said, patting her head comfortingly, "you couldn't know. A woman of your background doesn't know about these things. It's a side of life you've never seen."

"Oh, Dr. Chadwick," Betsy pleaded, drawing back from him and looking up into his eyes, "would you please help me? Will you take me away from this?"

"Why, certainly, Mrs. Hoover! Get your things together and we will leave this instant!"

"My things? No, I cannot bear to go up those stairs again! Let us leave now!" She took his hand and drew him to the door. "I do not want to spend another second in this awful circumstance!"

It was thus that Betsy came to live on "Millionaire's Row," or on what a writer of the period had called "the most beautiful street in the world," Euclid Avenue. Her rescuer refused to hear of her going to a hotel at the late hour when they fled the brothel and persuaded her to accompany him to his home at the corner of Euclid and Genesee.

Once there, he decorously showed her to a bedroom and withdrew. It took only a glance for Betsy to guess that she was in his former wife's room. However, since her mind was already racing ahead towards a newly-found goal, it did not seem too illogical a place to be sleeping!

In the morning Betsy waited until she was sure he had left the house before she appeared. The maid had her breakfast ready. After making good use of that—for she had formed a habit of eating a hearty meal once the night was over at the brothel—Betsy told the girl she thought she might feel better if she got some air.

By a roundabout route, she returned to the brothel, woke a couple of the girls and announced that her sister had just had a heart attack. After picking up such personal belongings as would not seem out of place on Euclid Avenue and borrowing the train fare to Akron from the girls, she dashed over to the house on Franklin Avenue and explained as clearly as she could to her mother and sister that they would have to head home to Eastwood for a while, taking Emil with them. Poor little Emil! He wept at the prospect of being parted, but Betsy promised him it would not be for long.

Having settled matters there and given her mother the train fare, Betsy left for Euclid Avenue and her new life, never to return to that part of town again.

That evening at dinner, she asked Dr. Chadwick if he would help her find a suitable place to stay. "Of course," she added sadly, "it will have to be modest, I'm afraid. Until I find new employment I am virtually penniless."

"In that case, my dear lady," he volunteered, "perhaps we could persuade you to stay here! The room you are in will otherwise stand empty for we no longer get visitors from out of town. And I must admit that your presence here is as welcome as a ray of light."

Betsy shook her head. "It is very kind of you. But it is not my nature to accept charity. If it were, I could call on my own father for help. But I have, it seems, inherited his strong vein of independence and am not inclined to take things for which I cannot pay."

"But you would be doing me a great service! For me, the pleasure of your company would be ample reward!"

After a little more of this sort of thing, Betsy finally gave in gracefully and agreed to stay until she found work.

After dinner, he took her upstairs to meet his mother and sister. If Betsy expected obstacles there she was disappointed. They barely took time to greet her before turning to him with their accounts of the day's twinges and complaints. She came downstairs wondering what had kept him so long from fleeing to the brothel!

A few days later, Betsy discovered in after-dinner conversation in the drawing room that he himself was not free of discomfort. For some time he had been bothered with mild attacks of rheumatism in his lower back and upper legs. Stretching the truth just a little, Betsy told him that as a girl she had been taught by an old nurse how to give massage and expressed the opinion that perhaps the occasional rub-down would help. "At any rate," she concluded modestly, "If you think it might ease your pain, it would give me a great deal of pleasure to try. And it would also help me feel that I was doing something to compensate for my accommodation."

Dr. Chadwick looked a little embarrassed. Yet, Betsy could see that the idea appealed to him. After some more discussion, it was agreed that he would retire to his room and that she would join him in her new role as a masseuse.

As it turned out, the location of his discomfort had a decidedly beneficial effect on expediting their relationship. He would have been a poor male indeed who did not respond to friction, however ineptly applied, on the lower back and upper thighs! Before long the sheer discomfort of being repeatedly rammed into a mattress forced him to turn over— and the treatment ended in a most satisfactory fashion.

The treatments were resumed the following evening and the following. At the end of the first week, Betsy noticed that he never mentioned his rheumatism again. But the treatments went on. Perhaps, in her humble way, Betsy had contributed something to medicine. It would make an interesting cure if universally applied.

Between treatments they talked of many things. He told her about his childhood, about his father who had also been a physician but of greater renown and, Leroy admitted, of greater ability than he himself. Leroy's father, Betsy learned, had struck oil on their Pennsylvania farm years ago, grown wealthy, and moved to Cleveland where he had built the house on Euclid Avenue as a monument to his well-lubricated ego. Leroy had had—as he saw it—a harsh childhood. If it had not been for the understanding and compassion of his mother, he could not have survived. (Betsy, who had sold her virtue on the stubble of a hay field at thirteen, found it difficult to project herself into an environment where a boy grew bitter because a family servant was always rude to him on the way to school!)

At first, when he asked about her own youth, Betsy put off answering, implying that a shadow hung over it into which she was now reluctant to peer. Gradually, however, she began to lift the veil and one night, when they were relaxing together after a particularly strenuous treatment, she decided that the time had come.

Swearing him to absolute secrecy, she told him the awful truth: she was the love daughter of Andrew Carnegie.

Some men might have scoffed. But not Leroy. He considered himself something of an authority on the unusual in human behavior. Indeed, Cleveland lawyers occasionally called upon him to testify as an expert on psychological matters. And one of his firmest beliefs was that people who lay together do not lie together. Besides, he had grown up in the world of "Millionare's Row" where the name of the great steel magnate was often heard. The John D. Rockefellers and the Hannas and the Andrews down the street knew Carnegie. And all of these families expected others of their ilk to have their peccadilloes, their little sins and sidetrips from the social norm—and accidental offspring were not unknown even in Cleveland.

Betsy went on, with many a heavy sigh, to tell Leroy how it all had happened, back in the days when Carnegie had first come out from Scotland, a poor immigrant boy seeking his fortune in the New World. He became a telegraph operator and then secretary to the Superintendent of the Pennsylvania Railway. At this point he was twenty-two. Despite the later appearance of ruthlessness that his progress gave, he was a man capable of great family devotion. However, he was so attached to his mother that he could not bring himself to marry. Fortunately, he found a woman who understood and out of their secret alliance Betsy was born.

At that early point in her father's career any scandal would have ruined his chances for promotion. He could not suddenly produce a wife and child. And that is why, Betsy explained, she was taken across the border into Canada and placed with a kindly family by the name of Bigley to be raised by them as if she were their own child.

"And did your father never come to see you?"

"Never. But I understand. And I feel sure that someday he will claim me for his own. Even now, I know from certain messages the Bigleys have been sent that he is taking steps to see that I will not suffer financially once he is gone."

"What about your mother?"

Betsy shook her head. "I never saw her after I was sent to the Bigleys. She never married. She died some years ago, still true to the young man she had loved. I—I don't even know where she is buried. Oh, Leroy, promise me again that you will never tell! Even though I have yet to meet him and know him as a man, I love my father and would not want in any way to hurt him."

"Of course, my dear. I understand. You can be sure no word of all this will ever cross my lips."

Wonderful Leroy! Is there anything more reassuring in life than a predictable person? While the Chadwicks lived on "Millionaire's Row," Leroy had never really been part of the social life of the great families. People who live on the edge of society yearn so for the center that they will do and believe almost anything that seems to draw them toward the core. Now through Betsy (or Cassie, as he called her), Leroy yearning to be accepted as his distinguished father had been, could feel some affinity with the Rockefellers and the rest. The fact that her qualifications for belonging were somewhat marred by the bar sinister did not decrease his esteem. (And perhaps her indications of eventual financial recognition by her father had not passed unnoticed either.)

The very next night, when they were in the drawing room after dinner, he suddenly dropped to his knees and begged her to marry him. Betsy had always derived somewhat more than normal pleasure out of seeing a man on his knees before her. And it had been her instinctive reaction to treat a man in such a position with tremendous scorn. However, she caught herself in time, raised him to his feet, and welcomed him into her arms.

CHAPTER SEVEN

I t was decided that to preserve decorum (Betsy's residence
in the house raised certain social problems) they should be
married in some other city.

"Do you have a preference, my dear? I will go anywhere
in the world so long as, in the end, you are my wife."

Betsy smiled at him fondly. "If that is so, then I am going
to ask a foolish thing. You know, dear heart, that ours will be
a quiet wedding—and it must be so. Your mother and sister
are not well enough to travel. I could not ask the Bigleys to
come down; it would not be right. If only my father could be
there! I wonder—does it seem silly to you if I say that I would
like to be married in Pittsburgh? Even though I cannot invite him to the wedding, just knowing that he is nearby will
somehow help."

Leroy grinned. "Where else should the daughter of Andrew Carnegie be married than in the city he has helped to build and make famous? Besides, I think I can contribute something. I have a cousin there who is a minister, and I know that he would be delighted to officiate."

Thus it was that on a cool February day in 1896 Betsy found herself standing in the parlor of the largest suite in Pittsburgh's Hotel Anderson being married by the Reverend A. H. Jolly of the socially-approved Concord Presbyterian Church, under the authority vested in him and confirmed by Wedding Licence Number 9647 duly registered in the courthouse at Allegheny where, presumably at the request of the bride, Cassie L. Hoover, it is marked "Don't Publish."

It was a great wedding. The best that Betsy had ever had. Leroy and Cassie left that night for a trip to New York. Leroy was in fine form. (She may have contributed to that by having declared, the night he proposed, that it seemed only proper that the "treatments" should cease until they were wed!)

All her life, Betsy had had a tremendous contempt for money—and a tremendous appetite for the things that money could buy. Now, at last, she had a man who could well afford to supply her with beautiful things. Their honeymoon became one long shopping trip. When they returned to Cleveland, they were followed by trunks of new clothes and furs and jewels (which Betsy allowed the servants to assume were all part of her normal wardrobe).

The one dark spot in the whole exciting experience was her meeting with Leroy's daughter, Mary. A very independent young lady, she had refused to attend the wedding, pleading the pressure of examinations. In consequence, they went up to see her in Boston on their way back from New York. She did not have her father's weak chin.

Betsy did not think for a moment that Mary saw through her. At forty, Betsy was a match for any girl her age. But Mary still loved her mother and was dismayed at what she took to be her father's disloyalty to his late wife's memory. Betsy made a note to face this problem later. There were more pressing things she had to do first.

One of these was to help her new husband straighten out his financial affairs. She had discovered fairly early in their relationship that he was no businessman. His father, perhaps sensing this, while naming Leroy as his executor, had left most of his assets tied up in real estate. Leroy owned property all over Cleveland.

The problem was that Cleveland was growing, and changing as it grew. What had been very fashionable districts in his father's day were by now fast becoming slums. The rental income was dropping. The buildings hadn't been kept up. It was time to act.

Betsy explained all this to Leroy. His first reaction was to want to summon his brother back from the family farm in Pennsylvania and have a meeting, but she persuaded him that there was no need to upset everybody. If he would let her handle the situation, she thought they could manage on their own. Since he and his brother had never been close, this approach appealed to him—even if he had some misgivings about whether a woman could perform adequately in that world of business which he himself found so baffling.

It was a simple matter for Betsy to enlist the services of impressionable young men to get her a thorough evaluation of each property and an estimate of what each would bring on the market. While the total of these estimates represented more money than she had ever seen before, Leroy was shocked by how much the family fortune had shrunk without his realizing it. (Cassie may have contributed to the

shock a bit by adjusting the figures downward before showing them to him.)

Frightened by the prospect of poverty and distressed lest
his more affluent neighbors should learn of it, he was quick
to agree when she suggested that the first step was to transfer
all the properties into her maiden name so that, when they
were sold, no one would know that Dr. Leroy Chadwick of
8206 Euclid Avenue was involved.

Mrs. Cassie Chadwick had a little trouble with his lawyer
over that one. Betsy suspected that he smelled a rat. However,
she and Leroy decided that part of the blame for the sad
state of things had to rest on that very man because he hadn't
seen fit to warn Leroy years before. Within a week they had
a new lawyer, a man of her choosing, and things began to
move more quickly.

One by one the properties were sold. Their bank account
began to grow with the proceeds. It gave Betsy a great deal
of pleasure to see the happiness on Leroy's face when she
could show him the growing balance. Of course, she had
taken the precaution of opening another account in another
bank in her own name—and that was growing nicely, too.

With some money on hand, Betsy moved her attention to
another problem. From the first night when Leroy had
rescued her and brought her home, she had been depressed
by the decor of his house. The place was dark and dingy and
quite unworthy of a man of his position. Yet she knew that
if she tried to change or replace individual items she would
be struggling with the specter of his first wife.

There seemed to be only one course of action: to clean up
the whole mess in one fell swoop. Just when Betsy was wondering how to pull it off, Leroy's mother obligingly came to
her assistance by passing on. The brother returned to Cleveland for the quiet funeral and, to Betsy's great joy, volun-

teered to take his ailing sister to live on the farm. Suddenly, there was a reason to make changes in the house.

Without telling Leroy, Betsy went on a shopping spree. She bought furniture, drapes, lamps, dishes. She booked painters and paperhangers and rug layers. She and Leroy had had a long-standing theater and dinner engagement with another couple on Christmas Eve. When they returned, it was to a new house.

Gone in one hectic evening was every vestige of the past—carted off to be sold. When Leroy opened the front door and went in he was stunned. The workmen had done an excellent job.

"Look, darling!" Betsy exclaimed. "My Christmas present to you!" He went from room to room, too overcome to speak. Even the antimacassars on the new chairs were new. The only familiar thing he could find was his book collection. Betsy had thought it expedient to leave him that. Besides, she had not had either time or inclination to buy other books to fill the new shelves.

Mrs. Leroy S. Chadwick of 8206 Euclid Avenue. What fun it was! Expensive fun, of course! But that was no problem at first. So long as Leroy's money lasted, Cassie was as free with it as Lydia had been with Joe's in Toledo, or with Wallace Springsteen's medical earnings.

Unfortunately, even Leroy's considerably larger supply could not outlast Cassie's urge to spend.

She went on to add to the contents of their refurbished home on a lavish scale. After a while, word of her extravagance began to spread, and the press reported excitedly that:

> anyone who ever had been admitted to the house had stood spellbound on the threshold. Every room is simply a storehouse for valuables. Everything in the line of decorations is of solid gold. One of her fads has been

clocks, of which the house contains a collection large enough to stock a store. The principal one in the collection apparently is made of gold and stands three feet high. It occupies the centre of the parlour.

Watteau cabinets, of which there are at least half a dozen, are filled with rare carvings and statuettes and enough other small ornaments to fill a freight car. If there is anything so ornate as to be beyond description, it would seem to find its home in the halls and living rooms and boudoir of the Chadwick residence on Euclid Avenue.

As might be expected of a man in love, Dr. Chadwick was quick to introduce his new wife to old friends. Many contacts were made through the church to which his family had belonged for many years. Inevitably, invitations poured in and return invitations to visit the Chadwicks followed. For a time, it seemed to Leroy that the house was as it had been when his first wife had kept it filled with merry company.

A difference soon became apparent, however.

His first wife had been the daughter of one of the oldest families in Cleveland. She had moved with ease through the social structure of the city. Cassie had to approach society from the outside, improvising, imitating, playing a part. Thus, there was always something odd about visits to the Chadwicks. Guests felt that they had inadvertently stepped on a stage.

The marriage itself had a mystery about it and guests soon learned, as they dined amid the opulence, not to talk about the Chadwicks' past or even to venture such little ploys as, "And where did you and Leroy first meet?" Such attempts to probe drew frowns from the doctor and a glance of haughty reproof from his jewel-laden wife.

154

No matter how people tried, no information on how the marriage had come about was forthcoming. People took their curiosity home with them and smothered it in the civility in which they had been reared.

Given the sense of uneasiness the mystery produced and the sense of unreality that pervaded an evening in what one husband termed "the Chadwick museum," it was not strange that after the first round of visits and reciprocal visits, invitations for Leroy and his colorful Cassie became infrequent.

Cassie's response to this was pure Betsy; she ignored the implications, refused to recognize the snubs, and went on inviting people to her place.

Now, however, the kind of people she invited began to change. Cleveland did not lack people who felt flattered to be invited to a home, any home, on Euclid Avenue. And if that home was beginning to attract attention for the richness of its contents, curiosity as well as social climbing became a motive for acceptance.

As Cleveland newspaper readers were to learn later, ". . . Mrs. Chadwick is of society in Cleveland in a way, but not in it. The Chadwick residence is in Euclid Avenue, to be sure, but wealth may buy a house among the fashionables, whereas it may not, under all circumstances, enter society's sacred portals. The social path of Mrs. Chadwick has been stormy, her efforts to break into the exclusive set have not been crowned with great success."

Cassie had long ago discovered the disadvantage of reality: it was not malleable like fantasy. Eschewing the reality of what people thought, she saw herself now as the gracious lady of wealth. She was reported as being always "royally bedecked with diamonds" and her gowns were termed "lavish and expensive." No longer did she have to talk down to waiters and clerks in order to impress them with her position.

Now she did it with casually-dispensed largesse. She lived only in the present and a wonderful present it was!

She had maids and a housekeeper and a carriage drawn by a matched pair of shining black horses. When she entered a store the manager would excuse himself from other customers to serve her.

Gradually, she began to form a group of friends. It was small and, in its way, select, consisting of young women of good bearing if not social position who caught her eye and were impressed to be sought out by an older, wealthy woman.

Towards the members of this little coterie she was generous to the point of embarrassment. On one occasion she entered a piano store and, having selected a grand piano with ornately carved legs, asked, "Is this the only one you have of this design?"

"No, Mrs. Chadwick," the manager answered, "there are seven more in our store room."

"Fine!" said Cassie with a regal wave of her ring-clad hand, "I shall take all eight."

Later that week, eight of her young friends were confronted with the problem of where to put a concert-sized grand. Some of them, it is sad to report, made a deal with the store and took cash instead.

One evening in the fall of 1898, she assembled her little group for dinner in the Chadwick home. Leroy who, although not unappreciative of feminine charm on a one-to-one basis, was always dismayed at confronting it in quantity, had been forewarned and had gone off to his club. As soon as all had arrived and were sipping sherry in the parlor, Cassie announced, "Dear friends! Tonight I have a surprise for you. Next week I am leaving on a tour of Europe!"

"Oh Cassie, that's wonderful!" one of the girls responded. "But we will certainly miss you!"

Cassie smiled at them all fondly. "No, you won't. Here," she said, holding up a sheaf of envelopes, "these are your tickets. You are all coming with me! We have a car of our own on the train to New York next Wednesday night. Thursday night you will be rocked to sleep by the waves on the broad Atlantic. A friend of mine, Mr. Cunard, has made all the arrangements for your staterooms."

The newest member of the group, a petite, dark-haired little thing called Mirabelle, came over and kissed her.

"Darling Cassie," she said gently, stroking the carefully-arranged locks of her benefactor. "You must know some of us have work we must do."

Cassie nodded. "I have called on each of your employers personally and have arranged for your absence."

"But we can't afford it!"

Cassie grasped the hand on her hair and kissed it. "Bless you, Mirabelle, but this is a present! Each one of you will come back from Europe richer than she went away! New dresses, new hats, all the latest things from London and Paris. Why, who knows," she laughed, "one of you might even catch a count!"

"Now!" she cried, clapping her hands for the maid, "Let us go in to dinner and discuss the trip. After dinner I have another surprise for you."

None of the girls had ever been abroad before. Indeed, most of the eight had never had occasion to cross the borders of Ohio. The meal hardly got eaten as the excitement built. When it was finally over, Cassie, who always ate sparingly anyway and had been sitting back enjoying their elation, stood up and beckoned them to follow her.

"It's time for our last surprise for tonight," she announced, leading them up the broad center stairs to the second floor. Along the wall of the upstairs hall were arranged eight shiny new trunks, the brass fittings on their curved tops shining in the glow of the candles in the wall sconces.

"Each trunk has a name on it," explained Cassie. "Find yours and open it!"

Immediately, the air was filled with such cries of joy and surprise, such a cacophony of female excitement, that had Leroy returned at that moment, he would undoubtedly have turned and bolted back to his club.

"All right, girls! All right!" called Cassie, as they stood about holding up the finery found in their trunks, "Now we must make sure that your new travel wardrobes all fit. Come, we will use my bedroom. Each of you must try on everything, starting from the skin out. We'll take one girl at a time and the rest can help her put on and take off her things.

"Mirabelle, you be first. Here," she said gently as the little girl hesitated, "let me help you undo your bodice."

The trip went well. Everywhere they went, the eight pretty girls and their brown-haired patron with her wise smile and deep, all-seeing eyes, found a welcome beyond their dreams. It wasn't so much the novelty of American tourists that caught the fancy of the French or stirred the people of Rome, but the fact that they were girls, pretty girls, travelling alone in a day when women were rarely seen unescorted. Even in England, there was a story in the press that managed to convey, politely of course, that this group of Americans was, well, different.

One girl did, in fact, meet royalty. Not a count, admittedly, but nonetheless a genuine royal person who saw to it that she had a very satisfactory experience with a peer of the realm. Mirabelle, on the other hand, had a torrid affair with a young sailor on the ship coming home and, having been caught in the act by Cassie who came to her stateroom late one evening, was never again part of the group in Cleveland.

158

In truth, the group did not assemble often after the trip, for, as Cassie quickly discovered after landing, their voyage marked the end of a phase in her life. To Leroy's surprise (for he had relied on her) and to Cassie's dismay, the Chadwicks were broke.

Not only were they broke but, as soon as the bills from European stores would start to arrive by the blessedly slow sea mail, they would be uncomfortably in debt.

Cassie, as always, took such news in her stride—and her stride led her, logically, to a bank. Where else does one go for money? For good tactical reasons the bank she selected was the Citizens Bank of Oberlin, Ohio.

If people in Cleveland were impressed with her Euclid Avenue address, its impact in the little college town of Oberlin had to be even greater. Certainly she had no difficulty in getting the bank's president, C. B. Beckwith, to lend her money although she made it very clear to him that he should not expect any additional business in the future on the strength of one small convenience loan.

After all, her real purpose for visiting Oberlin was not to see him but the bursar of Oberlin College. As she explained to Beckwith, for reasons she could not disclose she wanted to give that school an endowment. Unfortunately, her personal funds were all tied up at the time and so, if he would advance the money, she would turn it over to the school and give him a note in exchange.

Since no collateral except her note was involved, Beckwith did not feel it was properly a bank matter but rather than turn away so potentially profitable and distinguished a customer, he advanced the money out of his own account. Cassie thanked him when he explained why he was handling it that way and insisted that his check be made out to the college.

While waiting for the note to be prepared, they chatted.

Beckwith, fat and balding at sixty-five, found himself drawn to Cassie and not a little flattered that she seemed to like him.

"Oh, how I wish I had someone like you to counsel me!" she exclaimed at one point. "I'm so vague about money matters! Unfortunately, Leroy, my husband, understands such things even less. And now that I know who I am . . ." She put a dainty hand to her lips. "Oh, I shouldn't have said that! Isn't it just like a woman not to be able to keep a secret? Well," she hesitated, "I suppose I have to finish now that I've started." She was sitting across his desk from him and leaned forward to cover his hands with hers. "If I tell you my secret will you promise on your word as a gentleman never to repeat it to anyone?" Her deep, dark eyes held his with an intense and compelling stare.

Beckwith swallowed. "Of course, Mrs. Chadwick."

"Well," said Cassie, "once upon a time, a young man arrived in this country from Scotland. The only work he could find was as a clerk in a railway office. After a while he met a girl and they fell in love.

"Unfortunately, her parents would not allow her to marry a lowly immigrant. But out of their love, a child was born, a little girl. In those days, Mr. Beckwith, the world dealt harshly with illegitimate children. Rather than see their little daughter grow up among people who would treat her badly, the young man arranged for her to be put in a humble but good family who lived on a farm in Canada.

"Time went by. The young man began to move up in the world. The girl he had loved died of consumption or, some say, heartbreak. And their little daughter grew up unaware that she was not the true child of her foster parents.

"When she was old enough, she left home and came to the United States. In due course she married and married well. Then, one day just a few years ago, she was visited by a solicitor who said that he had been looking for her for a long, long time. He told her about her true parents—and you can imagine what a shock that was! Then he went on to say that her real father, now getting on, wanted to provide for her and ensure that she should not be in want and also that, on his death, she would share in his estate.

"It was a very strange conversation, Mr. Beckwith. I, the woman, the girl, the baby born out of wedlock, could not at first understand why, if my real father was so concerned for me, he did not wish to come forward.

"However, the solicitor was able to explain it. That immigrant boy who was once thought unsuitable to marry my mother has become one of the great men of our country. He had married in later years and knew that if I were to be acknowledged, the publicity would injure not only us but also his family and my husband. While he did want to see me, all matters had to be handled with discretion. I promised the solicitor that I would keep all this secret. But now," she smiled sadly, "here I am telling you. Even my husband doesn't know. But I sense in you a trustworthy person. And I must confess that I feel better for having been able to tell someone."

Beckwith was touched. He grasped the little hands that had covered his, and gave them a reassuring squeeze.

"You have seen your father?"

Cassie nodded. "Only once—but that made up for all the lost years. We talked for hours! At the end, he gave me two notes for very large sums, one of which falls due next year. Until it does, I find myself, as today, having to arrange my affairs in anticipation. To put it frankly, while we do live on Euclid Avenue, my husband's management of his money has not been as careful or successful as it might have been. His mind is off in the world of medicine, I'm afraid.

"However, in January when my father's first note becomes

payable—it's for a quarter of a million—our problems will be behind us, for he has promised that there will be further notes like that as well as stocks and bonds. The problem is to find ways of getting them to me without people becoming aware of our relationship. That is why, for example, he is using the notes. They make it look as though he owed me money for something."

Beckwith nodded. It was a strange tale, but who could doubt those frank eyes, that open face, that shy and hesitant voice?

"Does your father live in Cleveland?"

Cassie looked surprised. "Oh, I didn't tell you, did I? No, he's in Pittsburgh much of the time although he makes his home in New York. His name is Carnegie, Andrew Carnegie. Have you heard of him?"

To a man in Mr. Beckwith's business that was like asking a priest if he had ever heard of Jesus.

"You are Andrew Carnegie's daughter?" he exclaimed, then glanced around, aware that his voice had risen.

Cassie nodded. "I don't understand how he did it, but the young telegraph operator worked his way up so now, I suppose, he owns the railway, among other things."

"Among other things," agreed Beckwith dryly, "including half the United States!"

"I'm very proud of him," said Cassie. "But now you see why what I have told you has to remain a secret. My father would be very angry with anyone who let it out. I imagine he could make it very hard for them."

"I assure you he could," said the banker. "In my case, you need have no concern. I have nothing to gain by breaking faith. But let me ask you; when you want to borrow money, why not use your notes from him as collateral? There isn't a banker in the world who would hesitate to let you have money on the strength of them!"

162

"Can I do that?" asked Cassie, her eyes widening in surprise. "I have the first note here in my purse, but I didn't know you could use somebody else's note to get money for yourself."

"Of course you can," said Beckwith, reassuringly. "It's done all the time. Why don't you just leave the note with me and we'll be happy to lend you money against it? Of course, we couldn't let you have the full amount for it. That's called discounting and we'd have to charge you some interest on the money you borrow because, after all, that's how we make our living. But you really shouldn't be without funds when you've got a promise to pay from the richest man in the country. Besides," he added reprovingly, "that's not the sort of thing you should be carrying around. You might lose it."

Cassie hesitated before opening her purse. "But if I give it to you, won't others see it and suspect our secret?"

Beckwith held out his hand for the paper, hoping he wasn't looking too eager. By coincidence, a quarter of a million dollars was the total capitalization of his little bank. "Don't worry. I'll put it in my own strong box. Nobody else will see it until it's due."

Cassie sighed. "I do hope I'm doing the right thing," she said as she drew forth a piece of folded paper. "I know so little about all this! Should you give me a receipt or something?"

Beckwith nodded as he took the paper and read it. "I'll give you one that just says you have on deposit here a quarter of a million in securities. We won't even say what kind."

A short while later, Cassie left the bank armed with her receipt. At the door Beckwith promised to deliver the check to the college personally, to save her time. Cassie thanked him for his thoughtfulness and headed home.

The next morning, she called on Iri Reynolds, the secretary-treasurer of the Wade Park Banking Company in Cleveland, to ask his advice. Would a bank like his be willing to advance money on the strength of a receipt showing that another bank had securities on deposit? Although Mr. Reynolds had never met her before, he had known the Chadwick family by reputation for years. He was quick to assure her that there would be no problem if she were willing to open an account.

By noon, Cassie was able to write checks on Wade Park up to $125,000. And did. She wrote one right away for a hundred thousand, went to New York on the evening train, and used it to open an account with the Lincoln National Bank on which, in turn, she wrote a check for three hundred thousand. This she mailed to Mr. Beckwith, asking him to use part of it to pay off her little loan and to deposit the rest.

She then went back to Chicago and gave Iri Reynolds a check on Beckwith's bank for $125,000. On the strength of her prompt settlement, Reynolds let her have a new loan for $350,000—of which she sent $300,000 to New York in time to beat the arrival there of the check deposited in Oberlin.

If the reader is a little confused by this whole maneuver, it may be consoling to know that you had good company at the time. It took Messrs. Beckwith, Reynolds, and the staff at Lincoln National in New York weeks to straighten it out. By then Cassie was back at the same game but with more players.

It was not an easy game. It always had to have new participants and the pot had to keep growing. Out of the Beckwith-Reynolds-Lincoln round Cassie had skimmed off $75,000, but she knew that eventually this would have to be replaced. That meant fresh loans and, if she was to have enough money to support her opulent life style, the loans had to get bigger.

Neither the first woman nor the last to have observed how effective it could be to go to a man for advice, she returned to Oberlin and closeted herself with Mr. Beckwith.

Her long-standing ability to shed tears to order came into play as she explained her new predicament. "My father is very angry with me," she sobbed. "I shouldn't have told him I gave you that note. Can I have it back?"

"Well, no, Mrs. Chadwick. At least not right away," said Beckwith uncomfortably as he watched his new silk handkerchief become a damp ball in her hands. "There's some problem I don't understand yet with the Wade Park Bank in Cleveland and Lincoln National in New York. It seems to me," he commented gently, "that perhaps you have been a little careless in the way you keep track of where your money is."

"I know! I know!" sobbed Cassie, "It's all so confusing for a woman! Yet I must have more money to see me through until Papa can take care of me. That's why I've come to you. You're so kind and understanding and so wise. Tell me, Mr. Beckwith—is it Charles?—tell me, Charles, what should I do?"

The bank president ran a pudgy hand over his shiny pate. "Um," he said after a moment. "Um."

"Yes," prompted Cassie, her eyes full of trust and hope.

"Well, maybe," said Charles. "Maybe we could do it this way. I can't let you have any sizeable amount without explaining it to my directors. But Oberlin College has some money on deposit here in an endowment fund. Money from people like you. It's just sitting there. Since you yourself have contributed, we might get them to go for, say, $50,000. But," he added quickly, "only for a short time, and it would have to be deposited in your account here. Would that help?"

"Oh, Charles!" Cassie jumped up and went around the desk and kissed his bald head. "That would be wonderful! Can you arrange it?"

Beckwith nodded. "With your name, there should be no

problem. And I think it can be done quite discreetly. Of course, we'd have to ask you to be discreet, too. Can't have anyone thinking our little college has money to give away to ladies in distress, can we?"

"I won't tell a soul," Cassie promised truthfully. "Not a soul. And that money will be wisely spent, too. I'm not really a wasteful woman, you know."

Beckwith smiled and dared to take her hand. "I'm sure you're not, Mrs. Chadwick."

"Cassie."

"I'm sure you're not, Cassie. But you really do need someone to look after you!"

Cassie looked at him with her deep, dark eyes. "How perceptive you are! Will you be my friend and help me?"

Her hand was holding his now. The pressure was gentle but firm. Their faces were close together. His eyes were held by hers. "Help me," she urged gently. "Be my friend. I trust you. Say you will help."

"I will help," said Beckwith slowly.

"Good," said Cassie, releasing his hand and returning to her chair. "Now then, I can tell you something else. Because you are my friend and you are going to help me, I am going to do something for you. My father has asked me to handle a business matter for him. If you will take over and act for me, there will be a good commission which we can divide between us. The commission is one way my father has thought of for getting money to me without anyone knowing why he is really doing it."

Beckwith shook his head. "I don't think it would be right for me to take money he meant for you, but if you wish to pay me a fee... What is the thing he wants you to do?"

Cassie leaned forward and lowered her voice. "Do you know Charlie Schwab?"

"I know of him," said Beckwith. "He's a friend of your father's, I've read."

Cassie nodded. "And one of our neighbors on Euclid. That's why it would be easier if you came into this; I don't like dealing with neighbors. Anyhow, Charlie owns a building father wants. It's the Castle property, you know?"

Beckwith, already excited by the prospect of being brought into contact with one of the country's great industrialists, could only comment, "That big office building? Occupies a whole block!"

"I don't know what father wants it for, unless he's planning to move his offices to Cleveland. But I'm supposed to see Charlie and offer him a million and a quarter for it. If he balks, father says I can go to a million and a half—but I can't go beyond that without his permission."

"That seems simple enough," said Beckwith. "How much commission did your father mention?"

"He said I could keep ten percent. How much is that?"

"A hundred and twenty-five or a hundred and fifty, if you have to go to the higher price."

"So half of that for you would be over $50,000?"

Beckwith got up and went to his window. Through its grime the people passing on the street seemed fuzzy and gray.

"Cassie," he said after a moment, "I think I'd better confess something. You have said kind things about me—about my being smart and wise. Maybe you're right, to a degree. I've been smart enough to work my way up to running this little bank. But I'm also wise enough to know my limitations. A moment ago, I'll admit I was pretty excited at the idea of meeting Mr. Schwab and doing business with him. But I think we'd better face my limitations.

"A man like that would spot in a minute what I am; a

small-town banker. He'd eat me up like—like a piece of toast. And I'd probably cost your father a lot of money simply because, well, let's face it, I'm not in a strong enough position to take on a Schwab."

"Well, then," sighed Cassie. "What am I to do?"

Beckwith turned from the window and spread his hands. "Do? Do what your father asked you to do! I'll stand behind you. But you have to make the contacts. You go to see Mr. Schwab at his office. Forget he's a neighbor. Tell him you want to buy the Castle Building. Offer him, well, offer him nine hundred thousand to start. I doubt if he'll go for it, but if you come right out with what you're prepared to pay, he'll try and jump you anyway!"

Cassie made it clear that she was uncomfortable having to do it on her own. But if Charles felt that was the best way. . .

A few days later Beckwith's new telephone rang. He took the earpiece off its hook and cried, "Yes?" at the black little horn on the stand.

"It's Cassie, Charles," said the squeaky earpiece. "I've seen Mr. Schwab. He is willing to sell. In fact, he already has another offer. He wants what he calls a token of intent. What's that?"

Beckwith shrugged at the telephone. "I guess it means he wants some money down to prove you're sincere. Did he mention any amount?"

The telephone was silent for a moment, then it said, "Yes. He wants a hundred and fifty thousand. Oh, Charles, what am I going to do? If I don't handle this deal right for father I won't get the commission, you won't get your share, and he'll be very angry!"

Beckwith thought for a moment. Putting up a hundred and fifty thousand was a bit rich for him, but if he was going to make fifty thousand as a result the percentage of profit was not bad.

"We'll back you, Cassie," he said. "You give him a check on your account here and I'll send you a note to sign, just to make it legal. Be sure you mail it right back, though."

"I will!" said the telephone. "Oh, Charles, you've been so wonderful, I could kiss you!"

Beckwith smiled at the instrument and said with an unwonted lear, "I'll remember that, Cassie! Now, get over to Schwab's and close that deal before the other prospect beats you to it!"

Some weeks later, Beckwith's accountant drew his attention to the fact that Mrs. Chadwick had not returned the note she had been sent to sign. Beckwith tried to telephone her but the wire connecting Oberlin with Cleveland was broken. On being told that it might be several days before it could be repaired, he decided to go to Cleveland in person.

Not that he worried. Rather, he saw in her delay an excuse not only to visit the big city, but also to go with propriety to Euclid Avenue. After all, he was Mrs. Leroy Chadwick's banker. If he happened to be in Cleveland, it was only right to pay a call.

It was fortunate when he did so that he asked the carriage driver to wait. The maid who answered the door said that Madame was not home. Charles explained who he was and inquired as to when she was expected.

"I am sorry, sir," said the maid, "but we do not know. She has gone to Toronto on a visit. If the matter is urgent, you could reach her there. She is staying at the Rossin House."

"No. No, it's not that urgent," mumbled Charles, wishing he hadn't been so hasty in buying a new suit. "When she returns, please tell her that I called and that I would appreciate hearing from her."

He went back to Oberlin to wait. Cassie, meanwhile, was having a wonderful time. It had been from pure caprice that she decided to go to Toronto. She told Leroy that she wanted to visit friends.

What she really wanted to do was to re-visit the places she had last seen when she was poor. This time, she arrived in style. The suite she occupied was genuinely hers. The purchases she made were paid for with cash. It was a real holiday.

At Renfrew's she bought the only seal dress ever made in Canada. While waiting for it to be let out, she asked a clerk if they had any "receiving rugs." When he seemed puzzled by the term, she explained graciously that when one is receiving guests it is desirable to have a small rug on which to stand. After examining what they had that might serve this special purpose, she chose a fur rug trimmed with foxtails. Her bill for the dress and rug was three thousand dollars. At that time you could buy a house for less.

If the clerks at Renfrew's felt it had been a good day, those at Ryrie's, still the fashionable jewellers, must have felt blessed indeed.

Incredible as it may seem, before she was through there she had bought fifty-six diamond rings! "Just little gifts for my friends," she explained. And one salesman, on the strength of a sketch drawn by the manager, left on a twelve thousand mile trip to buy her a diamond worth three thousand dollars. A fortunate columnist who stumbled on the story reported the stone to be "the largest ever brought into Canada."

It was obvious to everyone that Mrs. Leroy Chadwick was a woman of wealth—much of which seemed to be in her purse. She tipped extravagantly wherever she went. One Ryrie clerk, sent to the railway depot with thirty dollars to buy her a ticket back to Cleveland, offered her twelve dollars in change on his return and had it airily refused.

Leroy met her at the station when she got home and watched with both astonishment and alarm as porters carried box after box to the family carriage.

"It was a wonderful trip!" exclaimed Cassie, squeezing his hand.

He grinned back at her uncertainly. "Some man has been calling," he said. "Long distance from Oberlin. A Mr. Beckwith."

"Oh, him!" said Cassie contemptuously, "a little man. The local banker. I don't know why these people keep pestering us for our business. Have you had any interesting cases lately?"

The next day Cassie telephoned Beckwith.

"Charles? I hear you came to see me and have been telephoning. How nice of you to show such interest!"

"I was worried about the note," said Beckwith bluntly. "You haven't signed it yet."

"Oh, that!" laughed Cassie. "As matters turned out, it didn't need signing so I tore it up."

"What do you mean?"

"Well, I took the money to Mr. Schwab just as you told me to. But the other bidder got the Castle Building, so Mr. Schwab returned my money."

"That's too bad," said the banker. "I suppose your father was very upset?"

"Papa Andy? Oh, he understood. He said lots of deals go bad like that. He has given me another, bigger one to work on."

"What's that?" asked Beckwith, trying not to sound too eager.

"I'm sorry, Charles, but I can't tell you. He has really sworn me to secrecy on this one."

"But I thought I was your banker!"

"You are. You are, dear Charles. I'll tell you just as soon as I can. Well, I have to go to a meeting now. Good-bye!"

Beckwith heard the click as the connection was broken and knew he was talking only to himself as he asked, "But what about my money?"

The black-stemmed invention, created in Canada not far from where Betsy Bigley was born, could give him no answer of itself. With a sigh, banker Beckwith went home, put on his new suit, and travelled again to Cleveland.

This time the maid admitted him—and what an experience it was! Never in his wildest dreams had he seen such opulence! Left to wait in the drawing room he could only gape. Beneath his feet were not one but three Oriental rugs covering the hardwood floors. At either end of the fireplace stood two pieces of marble statuary as high as he was. Two even taller vases stood before it. Oil paintings were hung, frame touching frame, right around the room.

A more discerning man might have noted that while some of the paintings were signed originals (including a Constable then valued at $30,000), the array included a row of six prints which had been given away with *The Youth's Companion*. There were also, he did note, several nudes in frames of pure gold. And in front of the fire sat a great cathedral chair made entirely of cut glass, ingeniously upholstered in sealskin.

When Cassie entered to welcome him, she advanced with the dignity of a queen. Her hand, heavily ringed, was extended in front of her. Beckwith had a momentary impulse to drop to one knee to kiss it.

This was long before Shaw's *Pygmalion*, and so the small-time banker was ill-equipped to catch the careful cadence in her "How kind of you to come!" She motioned for him to be seated—not in the cathedral chair, of course, that was not for sitting, but in a lesser, lower chair along the wall. Cassie

172

followed him to it but remained standing, so that he was forced to tip his head back and talk up to her.

"I've come about the money," he croaked; "we need it back."

Cassie nodded, "Of course!"

There was a pause while Beckwith waited for her to say more. She was standing so close that he could smell her perfume, a delicate scent. French, he supposed. His legs were apart as he sat there looking up. Cassie said nothing more but moved between them as she looked down into his eyes.

"I mean," said Beckwith, to break the silence, "I mean we —the bank—should get its money back."

"You will," said Cassie quietly, not removing her gaze. "You will. You are my friend, my banker. You will."

"But when?" Charles wanted to drop his eyes, to lower his head, but knew that if he did he would be staring directly into her most private area. A gentleman never spoke to a vagina. "You see, my directors don't know there's no note. It's —it's very irregular."

Cassie nodded slightly. "Yes, it is very irregular. But it will be all right, Charles. As soon as this new transaction goes through you are going to be very wealthy. All this talk about so little money is boring." She watched what was happening inside his mind. "Papa Andy will take care of you," she added. When she saw him blink she knew she had him.

"Would you like to see the rest of the house?" she asked, stepping back.

"What? Oh, yes!" exclaimed Beckwith, lowering his head with relief and pushing himself up out of his chair. "I must say this is a—beautiful room."

"Thank you," said Cassie, "Let me show you the dining room."

As they passed through the central hall, she motioned to an

inlaid table on which stood a large "perpetual motion" clock under glass. "I hope our guests don't think I am hinting by having a clock so close to the front door," she laughed. "Oh, I do want to show you this!" she cried like a girl, taking Beckwith's hand and pulling him toward a little stand at the foot of the broad stairs. "I found this in Paris this year. Look!"

The stand supported a golden cage in which a golden bird sat on a golden perch. As she spoke, Cassie pressed a little golden lever and the bird began to sing. Before Beckwith could register his amazement, she was tugging his hand again, leading him into the dining room.

They stepped inside the door. "What do you think?" asked Cassie.

Beckwith looked around. Down the middle of the sizeable room ran the biggest mahogany table he had ever seen in a private home. Its reddish wood gleamed with a high polish that mirrored the six huge silver candelabra standing on it. On his right, behind a solid row of velvet-upholstered mahogany chairs, the wall was completely covered with old paintings and glass-fronted, treasure-filled cabinets. The wall on his left had not one, but four mahogany sideboard cupboards along it, laden with large and ornate silver pitchers, soup tureens, and bowls of various sizes. Above the cupboards, the wall had shelves holding piles of plates. "Mostly Limoges," said Cassie lightly. "But you must see my new soup plates!"

She led him to the nearest cupboard and opened a door. "See?" she asked proudly, bringing out a plate with a thick bottom. "I got these in Switzerland. Watch!" She set the plate down on the table and then lifted it again. Immediately a music box device in its bottom began to play a gay tune. "It's very effective when the maids are removing six or eight at once," she explained.

Putting the plate back on the table, she pulled open a sideboard drawer. It was filled with knives and forks and spoons. "There's really too much of this set," she sighed, motioning to the other, closed drawers. "Nine hundred pieces. I really shouldn't have bought it! I much prefer delicate things. Like these," she explained, picking up a cup and saucer from a pile. "It's Chinese. See?" she pointed. "It's all inlaid with rubies and turquoises. Not a large set, but rather pretty, don't you think?"

Beckwith nodded dumbly. The fact was that his mood of being overwhelmed was being replaced by a sense of suffocation. Everywhere he turned there was so much!

"I know," said Cassie, reading his mind. "I sometimes wonder why I buy all these things. Look!" she illustrated, pointing to a far corner. "All those paintings piled there have just arrived from London and I simply don't have wall space for them! Would you like one?"

Beckwith shook his head. "Thank you, but I couldn't."

"Nonsense!" exclaimed Cassie, going over to the pile and taking up the top picture. "Here," she said, holding the gold-framed oil away from her and looking at it with her head cocked on one side. "This isn't bad. Not worth much, I'm afraid. It's by some man named Whistler. Grew up in Russia, they tell me. Maybe that's why it's so dark. Do take it. Go on, you'll be doing me a favor. As I say, I'm out of room."

Beckwith went back to Oberlin that day with the picture under his arm. His clerk hung it for him in his office. "That?" he would say when someone noticed, "Oh, that's a Whistler our client, Mrs. Chadwick, gave me. Mrs. Leroy Chadwick of Euclid Avenue in Cleveland? Charming woman."

CHAPTER EIGHT

C assie was, indeed, charming. She had never been more so—or needed to be more so. If Papa Andy was not as well informed on her activities as he should have been, a growing number of people were being informed about Papa Andy! Not openly, of course, for such a plant grows best in the shade. But the roots reached out, just as Cassie wanted them to do.

When she had told Beckwith that she was involved in a new, big deal, the only inaccuracy was in crediting Andrew Carnegie with having any part of it. The deal was wholly her own doing.

It started with a cup of tea, poured one sunny afternoon for the wife of a Cleveland banker. They had met once before but only briefly outside the Euclid Avenue Baptist Church.

On the strength of that, Cassie had invited her to drop in. The lady arrived at the appointed time under the impression that she was to be part of a social gathering but, if she was disappointed or alarmed to find that she was on a solo flight, she quickly forgot it under the stress of having to force herself not to stare at the Chadwick home's decor. There had been rumors but they really didn't do the place justice, she decided, as she followed the maid past glass cabinets full of bric-à-brac in the front hall.

Cassie came sweeping in to greet her dressed in a full-length velvet gown of dark green caught up in front by a bright yellow bow. Around the high collar of the dress she had hung a heavy chain of gold links on which were strung what appeared to be a collection of horse medallions. They clanked as she walked.

No one we know has ever termed tea "the great leveller." Yet certainly it had a calming effect that day on Mrs. Livesey and before long the two women were levelling with each other.

Perhaps the tea alone should not, of course, be given the whole credit. One must also recall the experience that clairvoyants such as Lydia DeVere had had in putting people at their ease and in getting them to reveal themselves.

Patience Livesey soon found herself talking about her husband in a way that no woman of her breeding normally would. In turn, of course, her hostess bared her own soul. The problems of running a large house; her relationship (still strained) with Leroy's daughter, Mary; the difficulties of being married to a man with such a demanding profession. And then, of course, there was her own personal problem. The one she could never discuss with anyone.

Mrs. Livesey's ears came forward at that. We all love secrets. Especially if they are secrets about the folks who live

177

on life's Euclid Avenues. She didn't exactly salivate, but Cassie certainly had her attention.

"Oh, dear," said Cassie with remorse. "I really shouldn't have mentioned that! But you know what it is like to have a secret and never be able to share it, don't you?"

Patience didn't. The only secret she had ever had involved puberty and that had been raucously revealed by her mother's laundress. However, she understood the principle of secrets and nodded sympathetically.

"Oh, dear," said Cassie again, "I wonder. Can I trust you? What a rude thing for me to say! I mean, I do want to tell someone. I think I would feel better if I did. But if I tell you, would you promise me never to repeat it, ever?"

"Of course," said Patience promptly.

"Well," said Cassie, dropping her eyes. "Even dear Leroy doesn't know this, but I am not who I claim to be. All of this," she waved her hand at the luxury that surrounded them, "all of this is nothing. Mere trappings. I live a sham life, Patience. A sham life." She dabbed her moist eyes with a handkerchief. "Someday, I know I will have to tell Leroy. But I want to spare him as long as I can, because I know that when the truth comes out it will change our lives completely. Do you understand?"

Patience thought about it for a moment. "No," she said at last, "I'm afraid I don't. What can be so bad that your husband won't understand? The Chadwicks are pretty solid, you know."

"That's just it!" cried Cassie. "Solid. Established. How will he react when I tell him that all this . . ." again she waved her hand at the decor, ". . . is but the trappings of a gardener's cottage compared to what's in store? Leroy loves this place. This is his home. But someday soon, I am going to have to tell him that I am wealthy. Not wealthy by Cleveland standards, high as they are, but wealthy by world standards. You see, Patience—and don't you ever breathe this to a soul as long as you live—I am Andrew Carnegie's daughter." She paused. A misgiving entered her mind. Did this mousy little woman know who Carnegie was? If she didn't, a lot of tea had been wasted!

"You mean Carnegie the steel man?" asked Patience, "the one the papers call 'the little Scot giant'?"

Cassie nodded. "That's my father. But no one must know because I was born when he was young and poor and, alas for me, single. Through the years he has looked after me from a distance as best he could. However, you know how people feel about illegitimate children these days. The whispering that goes on! I'll say this for Papa Andy; never once in all my life has anyone ever taunted me or called me bastard. That's how careful he has been.

"But now," she went on with a little sigh, "you know what's happening. There he sits, the ruler of our financial world. At a word from him, stocks go up or down. He's a modern Midas—everything he touches seems to turn to gold. The result is he is getting so much publicity and attention that he has almost been driven into hiding. They say there's just no way people can get past those secretaries of his and get in to see him."

Patience nodded. "Yes, I read the other day that he's become a recluse, shut up in his big mansion on the edge of New York."

Cassie smiled gently and knowingly. "He's not so much a recluse as you might think. He also has a place in Pittsburgh and comes and goes a lot more freely than people know. It was there I saw him just a few weeks ago. We had a long talk about the future. Death isn't a pleasant topic, but he insisted that we had to make plans. And that's the heart of my prob-

lem now, because he wants to pass over to me a large part of
the estate before he goes.

"As a matter of fact," she added, delving into her bosom,
"I got this letter from him just today. Here, read it and you'll
see why I'm worried."

Had her hostess, almost a stranger, pressed on her a piece
of private family correespondence under other circumstances,
Patience might have been a little embarrassed. But a letter
from Andrew Carnegie, whose name appeared in virtually
every issue of every newspaper, was not to be refused. She
almost snatched at it in her excitement.

"Dear Cassie," it began, "I am glad our mutual money
plans are moving along so well. I took that first five million
we discussed and bought you stock in the Caledonia Railway. The shares are being registered in your name and you
can pick them up from me the next time you are in New
York. By then I will also have worked out where best to
invest for you the next five. I am glad you agree that the
money should be turned over to you now and in small lots like
this. That way, we will avoid the glare of publicity falling on
you when I go.

"Take care of yourself, my daughter, and come to see me
soon. As ever, your affectionate father, Andrew Carnegie."

How like the man to sign his full name even in writing to
his own daughter! thought Patience as she respectfully re-
folded the letter and handed it back.

"Well, there!" laughed Cassie, "I feel better! I've finally
gotten up my courage to tell someone! It's fortunate that you
came, Patience, for I have really had a serious need just to talk
about it. Things go around and around in your head and,
somehow, just have to come out, you know?"

For the rest of that afternoon and until dinner was over,
things went around and around in Patience's head. She had
found a new friend and that friend had entrusted her with a

very personal secret. On the other hand, Patience had never before kept anything secret from her husband. Not that there had been much to share that had interested him, for he was a banker's banker and had little interest in anything that did not involve money. Well, this certainly involved money, thought Patience. He'll really listen to me this time. And he's discreet, bankers have to be. It's not as though I were going to rush off and tell another woman.

Her husband listened to the story over their coffee. And he was understandably sceptical until Patience told him about the letter. She had held it in her own hands. It was real and concrete evidence. What was more, she could recall enough of its contents to impress him. Andrew Carnegie! An illegitimate daughter! Five million dollars—and that just as a start!

"What? Oh yes! Yes, of course, I'll keep it quiet, Patience! Well, I'll be damned! That's the greatest yarn I've ever heard!"

A few days later he was just about to leave the bank to go home when his clerk informed him that there was a Mrs. Chadwick who would like to have a few minutes of his time.

Cassie entered with her hand extended. "Mr. Livesey? I'm Cassie Chadwick, a friend of Patience's. Perhaps she has told you about me?"

Livesey came around his desk to shake hands and show her to a chair. "Mrs. Chadwick? Oh, yes, of course! Patience mentioned that she had tea with you recently. Doctor Chadwick's wife, am I right? Good. How can I help you?"

"Well," said Cassie, folding her hands primly, "I need some financial advice and I thought you might be able to suggest how I should proceed."

"What kind of advice?" asked Livesey cautiously as he returned behind his desk. Damned attractive woman. But attractive women always made him suspicious.

"What to do with some money I have," explained Cassie.

"A—a friend of mine has made some successful investments for me. As a result I find I have a little over a hundred thousand dollars that should be put into something profitable, but I'm not sure what."

"That must be quite a friend," commented Livesey. "Is he a relative?"

"No," said Cassie quickly. "Let's say he's simply a good friend of ours who is high in the world of finance."

"Well, then," Livesey pointed out, "if he has been successful for you before, why not let him handle this?"

"Oh, I couldn't!" exclaimed Cassie. "He has been kind enough already, I mustn't impose."

Livesey leaned back in his chair. "I see. Well, do you have any ideas of your own about what you would like to do with the money?"

Cassie thought for a moment. "I did have an idea the other day." She hesitated and smiled shyly. "It may sound silly to you. Women know so little about these things."

"Try me," urged the banker. "Women aren't always fools."

"Thank you," said Cassie quietly. "Well, I've been looking at the mortgage and loan business here in Cleveland. And do you know what I've noticed? All the companies are big and, for the little person, rather frightening. I think there might be room for a small company that was friendly and really sought business from the small borrowers."

"Small borrowers are bad risks," objected Livesey automatically.

Cassie nodded. "Some of them, but by no means all. The average working man has every bit as much pride as you and I. And if we sew him up with a mortgage, the way real estate is heading right now we'd probably make more money by foreclosing than by having a good loan."

Livesey looked at her shrewdly. "That's a pretty tough approach."

"I beg your pardon?"

"I said that's a pretty tough approach."

Cassie laughed. "When will you men ever learn that women are realists? Now," she went on, leaning forward, "what I want is for you to find a small group of businessmen who'll go into this with me. It's important that they be men of considerable wealth because I don't want anyone to get hurt if this doesn't work. But I'll put in a hundred thousand if you can produce three or four men who'll do the same. You will get us someone to run it—steal a young, aggressive man from one of the old companies."

"We'll need office space and advertising."

"The office space is right here, at least enough to start with. You've got that area upstairs, next to the dentist, that has had a 'For Rent' sign on the window for years. It has been my observation that working people who need to borrow money are, for some reason, ashamed of the fact. Rather than be seen going into a ground level place marked 'Loans,' they'd be happier using a door that is also marked 'Dentist.'

"As for advertising, that is easily arranged. There are these advertising agents around who buy blocks of space in publications and re-sell them in almost any size or amount you want. I understand that some of the agents have taken to offering free help with the preparation of the advertisements. A friend of mine tells me that one of them, J. Walter Thompson, is particularly good at advising on what to say."

"Um," commented Livesey, his mind examining the larger issues. Getting others to invest would be easy if he could tell them the Carnegie story! Without it, asking someone to match a woman's hundred thousand in any deal—especially one the woman herself had thought up—was a waste of time. Oh, there were women people would listen to, women like that Lady Randolph Churchill who had just been in town promoting her *Anglo-Saxon Review*. But they were few in number and, by Cleveland standards, considered oddities. Women just didn't belong in the business world. On the other hand, perhaps what he was looking at here wasn't so much a woman as a pipeline into the Carnegie funds. If so, as the operating head of the bank it was his duty to go along with her and see what could be developed.

"All right," he announced decisively, "Let's try it! You put the hundred thousand on deposit here and I'll start looking for the other investors. Of course," he added cautiously, "they will want to know who you are and something of your background. You understand how it is." He looked at Cassie meaningfully. "Is there anything you would care to tell me that would be helpful in persuading them as to your, well, stature?"

Cassie looked back at him, her eyes full of innocence. "I don't know. You have my name. I think you know Leroy from the church. I have the money. What else can I tell you?"

Livesey scratched his head in embarrassment. "Well, you know, things like where you're from, who your parents are. That sort of information."

Cassie said quietly, "Your wife has told you of our conversation."

"Patience? Oh yes. Yes, she did say something. But just between the two of us, you know. She told me that she had promised not to tell anyone. But husbands don't count, eh?" He forced a laugh. "I mean, wives and husbands shouldn't have secrets from each other."

"Good!" exclaimed Cassie. "Then anytime I want to check up on you, all I have to do is ask Patience?"

"Well, no. No, I wouldn't say that. But—" he floundered and then decided to plunge. "Look, Mrs. Chadwick, don't be hard on Patience. I promise you your secret is safe with me. It's just that it would make helping you so much easier if I could tell these people I mean to approach about your association with Mr. Carnegie. I would, of course, also swear them to secrecy."

Cassie looked doubtful. "I'm afraid. Afraid of what it would do to Papa if the word got back. Oh, I should never have told Patience!"

Livesey, afraid that she was about to start crying, got up and came around his big oak desk to take her hand. "Now, now, Mrs. Chadwick! Don't you worry. If I do say anything, it will be with the greatest discretion. And, if it helps, I won't even say you told me—which is the truth for, indeed, you didn't."

Cassie looked up at him trustingly. "Well, I suppose you know best, Mr. Livesey. But do be careful. Not just for Papa's sake and mine, but for your own. Papa can be very—very angry when somebody does something to hurt him."

Livesey nodded and patted her hand reassuringly. "Don't you worry, my dear. I'll take care. Just leave your problem with me."

A few days later, Livesey telephoned Cassie and invited her down to the bank for a meeting the following morning. Cassie sensed that there was trouble. As soon as he hung up, she called his wife and invited her to come again for tea.

Naturally, when Patience arrived Cassie was careful not to probe as to whether she knew why her husband wanted to see his new client. That would have been rude. The only reference to money matters came when, in the course of chatting about this and that, Cassie suddenly exclaimed, "Oh dear! I forgot to go to the bank this morning! Not your bank, I mean, although someday that may be true. My present bank." She passed over a piece of paper. "Look! Papa Andy has sent me a check for some dividends! I should have deposited it. Well, tomorrow will do, I suppose." She took back the slip, but not before Patience had had ample time to see that it was indeed a check made out to Cassie L. Chadwick in the amount of one hundred thousand dollars and signed "Andrew Carnegie." "I hear the church is planning a garden party," said Cassie. "Are you on the committee?"

The next day Cassie found Mr. Livesey looking very uncomfortable. "This is rather embarrassing, Mrs. Chadwick," he began as soon as she was seated in his oak-panelled office.

Cassie smiled quietly, "Please don't feel embarrassed about anything, Mr. Livesey. Howard, isn't it? And you must call me Cassie. It's silly for Patience and me to be on a first-name basis and for you and me to be 'Mr.' and 'Mrs.' What is the problem?"

"These other men I've approached. Other bankers, actually. I think they're interested in your idea for a company. But not unnaturally—well, you know what men are, Cassie—"

"You mean they balk at doing business with a woman?"

Livesey nodded. "So, I've sworn each one to secrecy and told them about your connection with your father. I've even gone so far as to imply that you were acting for him."

"That's not unreasonable," Cassie commented, "I have never said that to you, but you have been clever enough, apparently, to deduce it for yourself."

Livesey looked relieved. "I'm glad I wasn't being dishonest. However, I'm afraid there's more to my problem than that. You see, when they pressed me to prove how I knew that what I was telling them about you was true, I'm afraid they had me." He spread his hands. "After all, I couldn't just say that all I had to go on was a story my wife told me one night after dinner!"

"Of course not," Cassie agreed. She thought for a moment and then her face brightened. "I have an idea! Would it help if you could tell them that you yourself had personally met

186

Andrew Carnegie and assured yourself that he was aware of the plans for the company and was prepared to back me in it?"

"It certainly would!" exclaimed Livesey. "Is that possible?"

"Oh, I think so," said Cassie. "I'd have to explain the problem to him first, of course. He doesn't see many people any more." She got up and began to pace the office. "It's a gamble. He may be very angry with me but I think I owe it to you to try." She paused and turned to the banker. "Normally, Papa and I meet secretly in Pittsburgh but in a letter I have just had from him enclosing a check he says he also has some securities he wants to give me and asks if I could come to New York to pick them up. Why don't you and Patience take the train with me tonight? In the morning, while Patience plays in the stores, you can come with me to Papa's."

Livesey looked doubtful. The stories about how well Andrew Carnegie protected himself from intrusions on his privacy were many. "You're sure it would be all right?"

Cassie smiled. "It can't hurt to try. If this is what is needed to convince those Doubting Thomases, then let's do it!"

By the time Cassie arrived at the Liveseys' hotel room the next morning to pick up the banker, Patience was already out shopping. Since it was her first trip to New York, explained Livesey, she had been anxious to see how the stores compared with those in Cleveland.

"I'm afraid she's in for a disappointment," said Cassie, wrinkling her nose. "However, I am sure she will have fun."

At her behest, the doorman summoned an autocar. Cassie gave the driver the address of Carnegie's new home. The house in which he had lived since marriage had grown inadequate and so, deserting the convenience of West 51st Street, he had built in the Highlands, way up on East 91st. At the time of their visit, the new brick mansion with the granite trimmings ("sumptuous but not ornate," one writer said) was not too well known. In later years, as Carnegie began to prove through his generosity that he really believed that it was "disgraceful to die a rich man," it became one of the most familiar addresses in America.

Conversation in the car was difficult because of the noise of the motor and the driver's frequent squeezing of the horn bulb as he steered his way around the carriages, delivery drays, and cycles that filled Fifth Avenue at that hour. Cassie smiled resignedly after a first attempt and leaned back, relaxed in her corner. The banker sat upright and taut.

Every now and then he would give his gray vest a tug. Each time that he pulled downward, his shirt collar for some reason would ride up so that one of its wings would dig him under the chin. Pushing the collar down meant that he had to check his cravat, which had to be followed, it seemed, by tugging down his vest. Cassie watched the cyclical performance out of the corner of her eye.

The cab turned in at last at the corner of Fifth and East 91st. "Here we are!" exclaimed Cassie, as the car halted in front of the door. "Aren't the gardens lovely? Papa loves to walk, you know. See the water over there? That's the city reservoir. You can walk right around it. It's two miles. Some days Papa walks around it twice." She leaned over and whispered in Livesey's ear, "You wait in the cab. I'll go in and explain to Papa who you are and why you're here, then I'll come out and get you." She gave his moist hand a squeeze and, without waiting for the driver to help her, stepped out.

Livesey watched nervously as she went to the door and pulled the bell knob. In a moment, the door opened a crack and he could see Cassie speaking to someone within. Then the door closed and she was left waiting on the steps. She turned and smiled at him and then faced the door again as it was re-opened and she was admitted.

Five minutes went by, then ten, then fifteen. Livesey stopped tugging at his vest, collar, and tie long enough to pull out his watch. Twenty minutes. The door of the big brick house opened and Cassie came out. She paused to say something to the person inside, smiled and then, with a gay little wave of farewell, came over to the cab carrying a large brown envelope under her arm.

"Poor Howard!" she exclaimed as she passed him the envelope and got in. "Such a long wait and for nothing!" She started to say something else but, with a glance at the driver, she put a finger to her lips and whispered, "I'll tell you all about it when we're back at the hotel."

Once in the quiet and privacy of the Livesays' room, Cassie explained what had happened. It was her father's secretary who had met her at the door. Since he was not aware of who she really was, he had gone to see if his employer would see a Mrs. Chadwick. Naturally, her father had said promptly that he would. He had the securities waiting for her, said Cassie pointing to the envelope that the banker still held, but when she told him of the man waiting outside he became very upset and protested that she should have written to him first. "How do I know this man is what he pretends to be?" she said he demanded. "The world is full of charlatans and deceivers, Cassie. You must always be on your guard. Had you written, I would have had my people check on him and then, if he is what he pretends to be, I would have seen him."

At this point, said Cassie, a long-distance telephone call came through. It was obviously of great importance. Her father blew her a farewell kiss and waved her on her way as he talked.

"I'm sorry," she said to Livesay, "It's my fault. I know I should have written first."

"Oh, that's all right," muttered the banker, a little miffed that the great man should have thought to question the authenticity of a third-generation Cleveland resident. "What do you want done with these?" he asked, holding up the rather bulky envelope.

Cassie took it from him, stood up and began to arrange her feathered boa. "I'll put them in my strong box after I look at them. I gather it's mostly the Caledonia Railway stock he promised me. He says I now have the controlling interest, whatever that means. Seems strange," she mused, "I've never seen the railway. Never even been to Scotland. And to think," she added, weighing the envelope in her hand, "that this one little brown parcel contains something worth over five million dollars! It's a strange world!"

A few weeks later, the Cleveland Loan Company, with Mrs. Leroy Chadwick as President, came into being. It had an aggressive young manager and a small staff. Mr. J. Walter Thompson proved to be unavailable as the advertising consultant, for he was a very elusive man, always rushing back and forth across the country in pursuit of business. But a Mr. Lord was found who seemed to know what was needed and soon advertisements were appearing not only in *The Plain Dealer*, but also in the smaller newspapers in the surrounding towns.

Before long, those who had invested were delighted to begin receiving dividend checks. Woman or not, Mrs. Chadwick seemed to know what she was doing. Livesey was especially pleased with his tenant upstairs. As the reports of growth she gave him blossomed, he got more and more money from people who wanted to own a share. And the dividends grew still greater.

Then one day an investor did what was by Mr. Livesey's standards an unforgiveable thing. Despite the return he had been getting on his money, this man demanded to see a financial statement.

When Livesey called Cassie to tell her, she became very angry. "Who is this person?" she demanded. "Where is he from?"

"That's what makes it doubly annoying," grumbled Livesey. "He's not really one of us. I let him in on the recommendation of a friend. He's not even a Cleveland man, but lives in Oberlin and uses the bank there."

"I see," said Cassie quietly. "Well, why don't we take the poor little fellow out of his misery? I'm sure we don't need his pittance if he's worried about it. Tell him we'll send him a check tomorrow for every cent he's put in."

Livesey called her back the next evening in some agitation. "That Oberlin man," he spluttered, "I called him but he has already gone and applied for a state examination of the books!"

"Can't we stop it?" asked Cassie. "There's nothing to hide, but loan companies aren't too popular with the press. I'm afraid they'll give us a hard time even though we are innocent."

"I'll see what I can do," Livesey promised. "But once the state investigators have a request like that they're hard to call off."

"Let me know how you make out, Howard," said Cassie. "I have to go to New York in a few days, but I'll be back soon and will look forward to hearing from you."

Later that evening, Leroy looked up from his paper, "Anything wrong, dearest?"

"Pardon?"

"Anything wrong?"

"Just the usual nonsense of the business world," Cassie assured him. "I don't know why I put up with it, except I know it pleases Papa that I am involved."

She sighed. "Involved" was certainly the right word!

Those silly, greedy men, always wanting their dividends! And now this one wanting to know where the money came from. Probably put up to it by old Beckwith. How could she supply a financial statement? There was none to supply. All of them put their money in and then she simply gave it back to them a bit at a time. So much for dividends! It was more like giving children an allowance.

Oh, the company took in money, certainly. The nice young manager saw to that. But that money belonged to her. After all, it was her idea, her company. So long as Howard Livesey kept bringing in new investors there was money on hand to lend people and pay dividends too. Publicity, bad publicity, would scare off new investors and then there'd be no more dividends and, what was worse, no more money to lend. Soon, when the present loans were repaid, there'd be no more interest coming in. Then what would she do? It was very sad. Just when they were adding a music room for Leroy's new pipe organ which was due any day now!

The next morning Cassie had her driver take her to the solid old Wade Park Bank where she had once gone before. An introduction to its treasurer, Iri Reynolds, was hardly necessary. Cassie knew that he was a friend of Howard Livesey's and suspected, quite rightly, that the fact that she was the head of the new loan company would be known to him. When they shook hands she also sensed that since she had last dealt with him he had become one of the quickly-growing number of people who had been told in confidence about her Carnegie background.

The episode of the revolving checks was forgotten. Beckwith, not Reynolds, had been the loser. Now, like every other banker in town not already involved, Reynolds had been hoping to encounter her. When she informed him that she wanted to turn over an envelope for safekeeping, he accepted it eagerly. Livesey's story of her call at the Carnegie mansion and how she had emerged with an envelope containing five million dollars in securities was very much in his mind. Without raising an eyebrow, he accepted her statement that that was what the envelope contained and, without opening the package, wrote out for her a receipt that read, "I hereby certify that I have in my possession $5,000,000 in securities belonging to Mrs. Cassie L. Chadwick and that neither myself nor the Wade Park Bank nor any other person has any claim upon the same. Iri Reynolds."

On parting, Cassie clasped the banker's hands in hers and said movingly, "Mr. Reynolds, you have no idea what you have done for me." For once, Cassie had made an understatement.

CHAPTER NINE

When she announced a few days later that she was going to New York, Leroy wanted to go too, but Cassie told him that his patients had to come first. He didn't have the courage to tell her that he didn't have enough patients left for that to matter. More and more, as Cassie progressed in the business world, it was Leroy who stayed home. What drive he had had as a young man was drying up. With every need more than satisfied by Cassie's seemingly endless supply of money, he spent whole days just sitting around the house reading or playing current ballads on the pump organ in the front hall. Occasionally, he would write a letter to his daughter, Mary, at school in Boston, but there wasn't much to say.

Cassie had told Leroy that if he needed her she would be at the New Breslin in New York. She had never stayed there before but had read somewhere that Chauncey Depew regarded it highly. On the strength of that, Cassie telephoned long-distance, posing as her own secretary, and reserved, "the suite you usually give Mrs. Chadwick's uncle, Senator Depew."

The former candidate for the U.S. Presidency was apparently a man of good taste. The suite turned out to be very satisfactory. Five large rooms from which one could see Madison Square. As soon as the maid had unpacked, Cassie ordered lunch to be sent up and placed a telephone call to Brookline in Massachusetts.

"Is this Mr. Newton? Mr. Herbert D. Newton? How do you do? This is Mrs. Leroy Chadwick of Cleveland calling. I believe you know the Boston lawyer, John Eaton? His brother, Reverend Charles, is our minister in Cleveland. Yes, a wonderful and dedicated man. As a matter of fact, it was through him that his brother was kind enough to give me your name. I have some money transacting to do and he thought you might be interested. Excellent! I am in New York at the moment, Mr. Newton, staying in my suite at the New Breslin. Would it be convenient for you to come to see me? How about five tomorrow afternoon? My maid will have tea ready when you arrive."

Newton, a shrewd investment banker, would not normally have made a trip to New York on the strength of so brief a conversation if he hadn't had good reason to do so. The reason was very simple.

Shortly after Cassie had obtained Iri Reynolds' magic receipt, she had called upon John D. Rockefeller's pastor, the Reverend Charles Eaton of the Euclid Avenue Baptist Church, the congregation of which she had joined after marrying Leroy. Cassie had confided in him about her Carnegie relationship and told him about her current embarrassment; with all those securities over at the Wade Park Bank she still needed a large, short-term loan.

On the basis of her general technique at that time, what Cassie was probably aiming for was a church-blessed introduction to Rockefeller. We don't know. But when the kindly pastor suggested other, less illustrious Cleveland sources, she demurred, saying that she did not want to have her problems locally known.

The next best suggestion that occurred to the Reverend Eaton apparently was that perhaps his brother, John, a successful lawyer in Boston, might be able to help.

The pastor promptly wrote to his brother, referring to Cassie as "a most estimable woman" (an assessment he apparently made on the basis of their meeting for, as he later testified, "Mrs. Chadwick never attended a church service . . . and has never given a dollar to our work, directly or indirectly . . ."). With his letter he enclosed, courtesy of Cassie, a promissory note for half a million dollars signed "Andrew Carnegie," and a list of the securities she said were in that brown envelope Reynolds had yet to open and which she now stated were worth seven and a half million.

With these impressive documents in hand, the lawyer called upon his banker, John Graham, president of the International Trust Company, and said that he wanted to borrow $200,000 on Cassie's behalf.

Unfortunately, Mr. Graham was a hard-headed Scot who felt instinctively that so canny a fellow-Scot as Carnegie was "not likely to be signing half-million notes that went begging for discount." After looking over the list of securities he announced abruptly that the interview was over and the matter closed.

John Eaton then turned to a client of his, a prospect more likely to be sympathetic. Herbert D. Newton of Brookline was not only a banker, he was also a deeply religious Baptist who had heard the Reverend Eaton preach at Boston's Tremont Temple and had been impressed with his personality.

Newton listened to John's story with interest. While the Euclid Avenue environment carried little weight in Boston, the fact that he was hearing of a business opportunity relayed through the pastor of John D. Rockefeller's church certainly had its effect. Thus, he was more than ready for Cassie when she telephoned.

Over tea, Cassie added the final motivating fillip: the story, told haltingly, of her true and natural father.

Newton was completely convinced and certain that, moving in His mysterious way, God had put him onto a good thing.

He promptly offered to give her his check for $79,000 and his own note for $50,000. All she had to do in return, he explained casually as he extracted the proper forms from his travelling case, was to sign back a promissory note for $190,000.

"That's rather a bit more than seventy-nine and fifty," Cassie remarked quietly. "I was hoping you could let me have an even two hundred."

"I did," said Newton, "to start with. But then in a transaction of this kind, the first year's interest is deducted in advance. Five per cent off two hundred thousand leaves one ninety, do you see? And the difference between one ninety and seventy-nine plus fifty is made up of the bank's commission and handling charges." He held out his check temptingly.

Cassie sighed as she took it, "It's all so confusing! But, then, it's only for a little while. Soon Papa will take over all of my affairs and I won't have to worry about such things as this."

The next morning, Cassie ventured into downtown Manhattan and went to the Lincoln National Bank where she apologized to the manager for the confusion she had caused before and deposited Mr. Newton's check and the proceeds of discounting his note.

She spent the rest of the day shopping happily, with her maid, Freda, tagging along under a growing pile of parcels.

The next day she was back in Cleveland and went directly to Livesey's office. "I have decided," she announced on entering, "that that man in Oberlin can be bought. If he himself goes to the state people, they'll call off the examination. Do you want to see him or shall I?"

"Well," said Livesey, "I suppose that I could, but you're the President of the company."

Cassie sniffed, "All right, Howard, I understand. I'll go. Tomorrow morning."

"Shall I telephone and let him know?"

"Indeed not!" exclaimed Cassie. "Our friend is in for a little surprise!"

The following day Cassie made the trip to Oberlin but instead of going to see her fellow shareholder, she went to call on her old friend at the Citizen's Bank, Charles Beckwith.

He was pleased and not a little relieved to see her—and even more so when she sat down at his desk and wrote out a check on the Lincoln National for all she owed.

"I'm sorry I've been so long in getting around to this, Charles," she said as she passed him the check, "but Papa has me very involved now. Perhaps you've heard of my little loan company?"

"Yes," admitted Beckwith, "I've heard of it. Is it going well?"

Cassie looked at him reproachfully, "You should know, Charles. One of your best customers here in Oberlin has money in it."

"Oh yes. Yes, that's right," the banker muttered, embarrassed by the knowledge that he had already counselled his customer to be cautious.

"Well now," said Cassie with a forgiving smile, "I'll tell you what I want you to do. I want you to go to him privately and, without telling him who you're acting for, I want you to buy up his interest. Offer him a ten percent premium."

"With what?" asked Beckwith. "Are you asking for another loan?"

Cassie laughed merrily. "Of course not, Charles! The days when I had to borrow from little banks like this are over. Look!" She pulled out the receipt from Wade Park. "Five million dollars, and more where that came from! If only you hadn't been so suspicious!"

Beckwith handed back Reynolds' paper respectfully.

"I'm sorry if you felt I was being that way—Cassie," he said humbly. "Once a banker always a banker, I guess." He forced a laugh. "Well, I'd better get after that shareholder for you! Is there anything else I can do?"

Cassie shook her head. "I'm afraid not, Charles. Mr. Reynolds is looking after my short-term financing now. As a matter of fact, I have to see him tomorrow to pick up some money."

"We'd be very happy to let you have it," said Beckwith hopefully. "How much do you want?"

Cassie looked at him for a moment, then shrugged. "Well, all right. Perhaps I'm being too hard on you. I need eighty thousand plus whatever you have to spend to buy that man off."

Charles excused himself and darted out the door. In a moment he was back. "Here's our check for the eighty. If you'll just sign this promissory note form, I'll fill it in for you

199

after I've made the deal. As soon as I know how much I have to pay, I'll call you."

Cassie went home in a happy frame of mind. She knew that the purchases she had made in New York—particularly that large painting for the new music room—had caused her to write checks on her new Lincoln National account far in excess of her deposit. But she had brought back from the Oberlin bank a supply of counter checks. Blithely, she filled in one for three hundred thousand and mailed it off to New York. That would hold them for a while! Meantime, the eighty thousand Beckwith had given her would do nicely to pay for the additions to the house, the new organ, and a few other little debts she had somehow incurred. For that string of pearls, for instance. Fifteen thousand was probably too much to have paid, but she hadn't been able to resist it.

Two days later, Beckwith telephoned to say that he had bought out the shareholder in the loan company. "Oh, thank you, Charles!" Cassie exclaimed. "It was very kind of you to be so prompt. By the way, there's another little thing you could do for me."

"Anything at all, Cassie," Beckwith assured her.

"Well, when I was in New York last, I'm afraid I was a little naughty and spent more than I should have. Of course, I paid for everything—but that meant issuing checks on my New York bank, the Lincoln, for a bit more than I had on deposit."

"Oh, don't worry about that," said Beckwith gallantly, "just tell me how much over you are and I'll send them a draft."

Cassie had been about to tell him that she had already sent a check, but he was showing such a desire to cooperate it seemed a shame to upset him.

"Wonderful!" she exclaimed, "Just add the amount to my note."

"How much should I send?" asked Beckwith, thinking in terms of his own wife's occasional splurges involving an extra new dress or a pair of high-heeled boots.

"Three hundred thousand," replied Cassie quietly.

Beckwith looked at the earpiece of his telephone set. "Three hundred thousand? For shopping?"

"I know," said Cassie sadly. "It is a lot, isn't it? But most of it was just for one thing, a painting. And a good painting is like an investment, isn't it?"

"If it is a good painting," Beckwith admitted.

"Papa said I got it cheap."

"I see. Well, fine. But your loan is getting to the point where we really must have some security. Have you got something you could let us have?"

Cassie paused. "Well," she said reluctantly, "I do have two notes that Papa gave me. Would those do?"

"How much are they for?'

"One's for two hundred thousand, the other's for three."

"Fine. Can you send them today?"

"I don't like to trust the mail," said Cassie doubtfully. "I'd ask Leroy to deliver them, but he has gone to visit his brother at the farm. Is there any chance that you might be coming to Cleveland? Perhaps you would have dinner with me?"

Beckwith hesitated, but not in doubt. He was thinking about what he would tell his wife. "That would be very nice," he said at last. "I'll see you this evening."

"Wonderful, Charles!" Cassie responded enthusiastically. "And don't feel you have to dress. There'll just be the two of us. Very informal."

Beckwith hung up the telephone and rushed home to get his new suit.

Later that night when, under the influence of an excellent meal balanced at either end by more liquid refreshment than

he normally would have consumed in a month, Beckwith
found enough courage to approach his hostess on an intimate
basis, he was pleasantly surprised to discover that, beneath
all those petticoats, there waited a very enthusiastic partner.
At first, in truth, he was a little taken aback, for it was not
the custom in his middle-class environment for the female to
be responsive. However, he was quick to realize that he was
not only out-classed monetarily this wonderful evening. My
God! he thought as the lunging proceeded, the rich *do* have
more fun!

As he was leaving to go to the hotel where he would spend
what was left of the night, Cassie handed him an envelope.

"Here are the notes I promised," she said with a smile. "I
hate to introduce business into so wonderful an evening, but
it would be a shame if you forgot them."

Beckwith nodded. "I almost did, you know." He paused
with his hand on the knob, "You really should have someone
to manage your affairs. A woman of your wealth should have
a manager."

Cassie nodded. "I've been thinking that too. I get so confused!" She looked at Beckwith standing there in his tight-
fitting top coat, clutching her envelope in one gloved hand,
his round-topped hat in the other. He was not a very attractive man, but she liked his eyes. There was a faithful spaniel
quality about them. "What about you, Charles?" she asked.
"Would you be my manager?"

Beckwith shook his head. "I couldn't leave my bank. Not
after all these years."

Cassie smiled. "But you wouldn't have to! Managing me
wouldn't take that much of your time! And, of course, Papa
would want me to pay you something. He doesn't believe in
charity. Would ten thousand a year be a fair retainer? Anything you made over that on deals would be yours to keep as

well; there'd be commissions." She stepped close to him and put her hand on his cheek. "You *will* look after me, won't you?" she whispered, her dark eyes fixed on his.

Beckwith swallowed and nodded.

"Good!" exclaimed Cassie, stepping back. "Now, off you go to that grubby hotel! Come back in the morning around ten and we'll talk like business people." She leaned forward and kissed him lightly. "It's going to be wonderful not to have to worry anymore."

As proof of his ability to manage, Beckwith shortly thereafter persuaded his cashier, A. B. Spear, to join him in lending her $102,000 out of their own pockets and subsequently gave her $700,000 of the bank's funds. Using the Reynolds receipt, he induced a Pittsburgh steel executive to give her $800,000. (The steel man may have thought it wouldn't do any harm to help the Carnegie error-apparent.) The Savings and Deposit Bank of Elyria went for $10,000. The First National Bank of Conneaut contributed $25,000. Oberlin College lent its former benefactor another $75,000. And so on. No one knows even today how much money Cassie acquired during this glorious phase, but a reasonable round-figure estimate is $2,000,000.

Much of it went into investments that Cassie hoped would show a profit quickly—quickly enough to pay back the loans as they came due. And a great deal of it went on her back or into the glory of confusion that abounded in her home.

Meanwhile, back in Brookline, Herbert D. Newton was developing misgivings. Since lending Mrs. Leroy Chadwick all that money, he had had nothing in return but heartburn. No interest payments, nothing. Silence. He felt like one of the Cabots and only wished that the lady from Cleveland was more like the Lowells. As the weeks passed, he not unnaturally began to question his own wisdom in having advanced the money so readily.

After several unsuccessful attempts to get her to respond by mail to gentle hints, he finally decided that, Carnegie's possible wrath notwithstanding, he had to get some action. He wrote a very strong letter stating that he wanted his money back.

A few days later he got a response. Dr. Chadwick arrived at his office bearing an apology from his wife for her delay in answering earlier missives. He offered as payment on the loan two checks endorsed by Cassie and drawn on the Wade Park Bank, each for $25,000. They were dated a week apart. The balance of the loan, said Dr. Chadwick, would be sent to Newton a week after the second check was due.

Unfortunately, when Newton's bank subsequently presented the checks to Wade Park for payment, they were both returned marked, "Not Sufficient Funds." Even before the second was thus rejected, Newton used the long-distance telephone to try to reach Cassie. He was told that she was in New York, staying at the Holland House.

He promptly summoned two of his lawyers, George Ryall and Percy Flint, and marched on Manhattan.

Cassie seemed to be a little cross when the threesome appeared at the door of her suite. Newton was in good form, for the second check had bounced back from Cleveland just as he was leaving, and he strode into her sitting-room waving them both in his hand. Cassie frowned at his belligerence, but when he made clear what had happened, her attitude changed abruptly.

"Oh, you poor man!" she cried, motioning to Freda to take their hats. "How upset you must be!" She sank gracefully onto a chaise longue, spreading her skirts with a flick of her beringed hands. "I suppose I should have telephoned you to warn you, but things have been happening so rapidly these last few days that our little matter slipped my mind."

She paused, and said to Freda, "Why don't you go down to the manager and see if that cablegram has arrived yet?"

Cassie waited until Freda left the room before continuing. "An excellent maid," she said as the door closed. "I couldn't travel without her. But some things are better confided to the fewest possible ears!" She smiled. "I know I can trust you, Mr. Newton, to be discreet and I assume that, as your lawyers, these gentlemen will respect my confidence.

"You see, I have sent my husband, Dr. Chadwick, to Europe to—" She was interrupted by a knock at the door. With a wave of her hand to indicate she would continue in a moment, she got up and admitted two rather harassed-looking men.

"I'm sorry, Mrs. Chadwick," said the first as he entered, "we came as soon as we could. But New York traffic has gotten to the point where I'm sure it can't get any worse!"

"It's all right," Cassie assured him, "our friends from Boston have just arrived themselves." Turning to Newton and his counsellors, she said, "This is Mr. Edward W. Powers and this is his associate, Mr. Carpenter, of Powers and Carpenter, Park Row, my New York legal advisors."

After the introductions were completed and everyone was seated, Cassie picked up the thread of what she had been saying, "I was just about to tell these gentlemen about Leroy's mission in Europe." Powers nodded, but commented quietly, "I don't think you should go too far into details."

"I won't," said Cassie, "but they have to know what's going on. One of my investments, gentlemen, is a railroad in —in middle Europe. My lawyers here know how I acquired it and I think Mr. Newton can guess. In any case, I have found recently that I have over-expanded on my investment program. That is why Mr. Newton hasn't been paid. And that is why my husband has gone to—across the Atlantic to sell the railroad. He will also be selling some other securities while he is there.

"The cablegram which I am expecting momentarily will confirm the closing of the railroad transaction and apprise me of the proceeds. It will be followed by the money, which is being cabled for credit to my account at the Lincoln National Bank here."

She leaned back in the chaise longue and spread her hands. "So you see, the matter has already been taken care of. Had you merely asked on the telephone, I could have spared you this trip and expense."

The senior Boston lawyer, George Ryall, smiled, and said gently, "Well, Mrs. Chadwick, if we didn't need to come, why did you feel your own lawyers should also be involved?"

"I am a woman," answered Cassie simply. "When I learned that there were three men in the foyer of the hotel asking to see me, I felt I should be protected and called Mr. Powers."

The other Newton lawyer, Percy Flint, shook his head, "There's something wrong here," he said to his client. "I think it only fair to tell Mrs. Chadwick that we have counselled you not to leave this meeting without a firm commitment for repayment."

"The cable should arrive anytime now," interjected Cassie.

"Well and good, if it does. But even if the money is deposited to your account, as you say, what assurance has our client that he will get paid? We must recall that two bad checks have already been passed."

"I know," sighed Cassie, "They were good when I wrote them, but I suppose I just got confused on my balance."

Powers held up his hand for attention. "I am sure you gentlemen realize that we are dealing with an exceptional situation here. The amount owed your client is really quite small in relation to our client's assets. Payment is just a matter of timing—and Mr. Newton is going to make a profit of a size I am sure he wouldn't want publicized through any formal action."

"That's right!" said Newton hastily. "Not that it's unfair, of course," he added defensively, "but this was a private arrangement and I would like to see it settled privately."

His lawyers looked at each other. "Well, in that case," said Ryall, "perhaps Mrs. Chadwick would give us written assurance that the matter will be settled in the next few days."

"Excuse me," said Flint, getting up and beckoning him to follow, "I think we need to consult. Mr. Newton, will you join us? If we may, Madame?" He led the way into her bedroom.

While Cassie waited, her own lawyers whispered together but she remained aloof.

"Well now," said Ryall as the Boston group came back into the sitting-room. "I think we have changed our minds. It is true that our client doesn't want to go to court if he can avoid it. This is not an ideal matter for the press. However, if we did go to court it would not be Mr. Newton's reputation that would suffer the most.

"In fact, Mrs. Chadwick, it would be extremely unlikely that the secret of your parentage would be a secret any longer. It would have to come out in any discussion relating to the security for the loan. And the minute it did, every newspaper in America would hear of it and you'd find your father and you on the front pages."

Powers jumped to his feet, "Just a minute!" he exclaimed, "That sounds remarkably like a threat to me. Are you trying to blackmail my client?"

"Sir," said Percy Flint, "We are members of the legal profession, not moss-troopers. We are simply laying the ground-work for a suggestion."

Powers sat down.

"To continue," Flint's Harvard voice went on, "there would be publicity that would be regrettable. And there might also be legal action taken that none of us want. I am sure we are willing, as gentlemen, to accept Mrs. Chadwick's explanation for the N.S.F. checks. But as I am sure Mr. Powers and Mr. Carpenter will tell you, Madam, justice is no gentleman. For whatever reason, you have broken the law and can expect the consequences to be quite unpleasant if we go to court."

Carpenter started to say something, but Cassie stopped him and asked, "What do you suggest we do?"

"Until such time as all the money due has been paid," said Ryall, "our client wants a complete assignment on all of Mrs. Chadwick's securities, here or abroad."

"But that's absurd!" cried Carpenter. "You want to entail millions for a petty loan."

"No loan's a petty loan when it goes to court," said Flint.

Powers turned to Cassie. "It would only be a temporary expediency," he suggested.

Cassie shook her head. "I feel that it is totally unnecessary. But, in any case, I can't do it right away. There's a complication. Some time ago I had occasion to borrow three hundred thousand from a Cleveland source. To assure repayment, the lender got me to give him a power of attorney. I have since repaid the loan, but he has refused to surrender the power of attorney, claiming that, with interests and discounts, I owe him eight hundred thousand. It is, of course, an absurd position for him to take and my lawyer for my Cleveland affairs, Judge Albaugh of Canton, is engaged in getting it cleared up now. But until it is resolved, I don't think I'm in a position to concede to this request."

"Probably not," said Powers. "Well, where does that leave us? My client is willing to assign, but cannot do so at the moment." He paused for thought. "I guess the best we can say to you, Mr. Newton, is that we are willing to comply but we will need a couple of days. Mr. Carpenter and I will consult with Judge Albaugh by telephone, then I suggest we meet again on the eighth. I don't think we need ask Mrs. Chadwick to attend that meeting. It would mean that she would have to remain in New York. For that matter, with her permission, I suggest that it would be only courteous for Mr. Carpenter and me to go to Boston and meet you there."

"On the eighth," said Newton, rising.

"On the eighth," said Powers.

As soon as the Newton group had left, Powers wanted to place a call to Judge Albaugh. "I think we should ask him to attend the meeting in Boston," he suggested.

"Perhaps," said Cassie, "but I would really like an opportunity to talk to him first. I'm afraid he's not as well briefed on this power of attorney matter as I implied. However, I'm going back to Cleveland tonight and can see him in the morning."

The next afternoon Powers received a telegram from Cassie: JUDGE ALBAUGH ILL STOP PLEASE ADVISE NEWTON STOP WILL SET NEW DATE SOON AS POSSIBLE.

On the advice of his lawyers, a skeptical pair, banker Newton decided not to wait. After trying to get Judge Albaugh on the telephone, he and his lawyers took the train for Cleveland. There they consulted with the local law firm of Carr, Stearns, and Chamberlain in the Williamson Building and, at the end of the meeting, left with them for collection the two checks acquired from Dr. Chadwick.

They then called on Iri Reynolds at the Wade Park Bank and demanded to see the securities alleged to be in his care.

Quite properly, Reynolds refused to show them without witnessed instructions from Mrs. Chadwick.

Foiled there, the threesome then took a hansom to Euclid Avenue. But all Cassie would tell them was that the debt would be paid as soon as the money from Europe arrived. Her statement was very positive.

However, her appearance of sincerity was a little marred by a suspicion the lawyers held that the man who entered the house and hurried off to a back room to play an organ might just be the same Dr. Chadwick that Cassie had said was over in Europe peddling one of her railroads.

To protect their client, Ryall and Flint got their local associates to try to obtain an injunction restraining Cassie and Reynolds from disposing of the securities the latter held. At the same time, to avoid embarrassment for their client, they enjoined the Cleveland lawyers to keep the matter out of the hands of the press if at all possible. Having done what they could for the moment, they went back to Boston, and Cassie hopped on the next train to New York on the trail of fresh money.

Time went by. Cassie kept getting loans to pay off loans and kiting checks. Her investment portfolio grew and became, in itself, a source of equity for further loans. But even though she had good counsel on buying stocks, she seldom made any money on them. Lacking profits and loving luxury, she was almost wholly engaged now in seeking new people to whom she could go for additional funds.

When it came to repayment, she did her best to avoid it. People like Beckwith and his cashier, Spear, were easy to handle, if you didn't mind putting up with a little hysteria. Others were held off with promises or, if necessary, some cash. And still others were simply ignored.

Unfortunately, one of the ones she put in the latter class

was Herbert D. Newton. Convinced now that it was not God but the Devil that had involved him in the deal, banker Newton finally listened to what his lawyers had been telling him all along and on November 22, 1904, brought suit in Federal Court, Cleveland, for the amount of $190,800. The suit also asked that the Wade Park Bank be restrained from disposing of the securities to the claimed value of $7,500,000 which Iri Reynolds held in trust.

CHAPTER TEN

As soon as word of the suit got out, the nervous system of the world of finance began to emit shock vibrations and everyone who had been involved with Cassie began to twitch. The American Exchange National Bank and the Euclid Avenue Savings and Trust Company rushed into the court to claim a total of $67,039. The Savings Deposit Bank of Elyria, Ohio, following with an overdue note for $10,000, almost got crushed in the crowd.

Over in Oberlin, Charles T. Beckwith, her would-be money manager, found himself facing his directors for having given Cassie loans equal to four times the value of the capital stock of the bank. The fact that he had also advanced her $102,000 of his own money did nothing to improve their opinion of his sanity.

Beckwith kept assuring his associates that all the indebtedness was well secured, for he held Cassie's note for $500,000,
endorsed by a man "who can pay it as easily as you or I can
pay a nickel." Being a gentleman as well as a banker, however, he refused to divulge to his directors the name of the
man.

"I can't tell you, I can't!" he cried when they pressed him.
"If I lose honor, reputation, everything, I must keep locked
in my breast this one secret. I am bound by an oath I cannot
break."

Unfortunately for Cassie, but to the delight of newspaper
readers across the nation, the attorneys for banker Newton
did not share Charles Beckwith's concept of honor. Their
client also had a note for $500,000, they revealed, and the sig-
nature on that note read "Andrew Carnegie."

With his name at last in the open, the reporters descended
on the steel king to get a statement.

The laconic Scot said only, "I know nothing of the
woman."

The woman herself suddenly became elusive. The reporters
quickly traced her to the Holland House in New York, where
she had gone on one of her shopping sprees, but the trail
ended there for a while. She had checked out and left no forwarding address. One newspaper ran a "think piece" suggest-
ing that she had committed suicide. Others picked up this
story, interpreting it as being based on fact and for several
days she was dead from coast to coast. Then, hopefully to
someone's chagrin, it was discovered that she had simply
moved over to her other favorite New York hotel, the New
Breslin, and was living there quite comfortably in her old
suite. Perhaps a little miffed at her demise, she refused to
see reporters.

However, there was no shortage of news coming out of

Cleveland. The judge hearing the suit ordered Iri Reynolds to bring to court the envelope he was holding for Cassie and to open it. He complied reluctantly. When a cursory examination of the contents made it apparent that he had been holding a pile of worthless paper securities, he sat down at the counsel's table and cried. The judge asked him gently how much of his own money he had advanced to Mrs. Chadwick, but Reynolds asked to be excused from answering that question and the judge let the matter drop.

A week later, Cassie was arrested at the New Breslin. To her dismay, she was whisked from its familiar luxury to the dank discomfort of a cell in the Tombs. It was all handled quite properly, of course, and not without some unusual displays of courtesy by the police, for they were not only dealing with a person of front-page importance but also of alleged great wealth.

In addition to that, she was obviously a lady. The policeman who made the actual arrest commented to reporters that she had "the kindest, gentlest face one would ever want to see. Just such a face as you or I would like to see in our families."

Actually, Cassie was feeling neither kind nor gentle. She was very annoyed. Stopped in the hotel lobby as she was being escorted out, she said to the reporters that she was being made a victim of circumstance. "Public clamor has made me a sacrifice," she protested. "Here I am, an innocent woman, hounded into jail, while a score of the biggest businessmen in Cleveland would leave town tomorrow if I told all that I know. Yes, I borrowed money, but what of it? I will even admit that I did not borrow it in a businesslike way. I wish now that I had followed old rules a little closer. But you can't accuse a poor businesswoman of being a criminal, can you?"

The next day, escorted by Deputy United States Marshal

Kumb, she boarded the train for Cleveland and made herself as comfortable as possible in a compartment of a sleeping car ironically named "Aida," after the Ethiopian king's daughter who was buried alive.

At the end of the line there was great excitement. The newspapers were having a ball. Even the Toronto *Mail and Empire* sent its sob sister, Kathleen Blake, to cover the scene and try for an interview.

Some of the problems in sorting out what actually went on during the ensuing days stem from the enthusiasm and imagination of the reporters. Without the Andrew Carnegie involvement, the stories would have been cursory at best; but the famous name attracted reporters from far and near. This wasn't just another lawsuit. It had everything a reporter could ask for, and the more you dug the more you found.

The only thing to be regretted was that Dr. Chadwick and his daughter weren't available. By the time the reporters got to the house, all the butler would tell them was that the Doctor and Mary had left that morning for Europe. Had the trip been planned for a long time? The butler didn't think so—and neither did the readers of the evening papers.

So good a job had the reporters done of exciting their readers that Cassie's arrival the next morning was awaited by large crowds at the Union Station. At the county jail a line of policemen was needed to hold back hundreds of people who were packed along the northwest corner of the Public Square.

FROM THE PAGES OF THE *CLEVELAND LEADER* THE FOLLOWING DAY:

Back home again, Cassie L. Chadwick, alias Madame DeVere, alias Elizabeth Bigley, the queen, the empress of frenzied finance, the Cleveland woman who has startled the world, declares once again that she will pay all her debts.

Just before she alighted from the Lake Shore train yesterday afternoon, she said to a *Leader* representative, "The world has had a sensation in this case, but there is still a greater sensation to come."

Pressed for more definite statement, Mrs. Chadwick, making a vain endeavour to suppress tears, said in a trembling voice, "I will make a formal statement perhaps tomorrow, perhaps next week, perhaps six months from now. The statement will involve my life from my first financial transaction."

As she neared this city, she turned to Deputy United States Marshal Kumb and asked, "What do the people think of me in my home city? Are they all against me? Will there be a crowd at the station to stare at me?"

She broke down and wept like a child. The next moment she had dried her tears and was chatting gaily with the deputy. It was very evident, however, that she was feigning this lightness of heart, for the deputy noticed an involuntary shudder and then came a flood of tears and violent sobbing. The faithful maid placed both arms about her mistress and implored her to be brave. From Erie, Pa., to Cleveland it was a succession of tears and smiles, the woman now and then gritting her teeth and clenching her fist to say, "I'll fight this case! It won't be long before the public knows the truth!"

When told by someone that a mob of several thousand people had already gathered at the Union passenger station in Cleveland, there was a hysterical scene. The wailing of Mrs. Chadwick could be heard through the partitions of the drawing-room in which she was concealing herself from the other passengers on the sleeping car. Eagerly she inquired if there was not some secret stopping place for the train where she could be taken off and hurried in a cab to the office of the

United States Marshal. When informed by Deputy Kumb that such a plan would be impossible because United States Marshal Chandler had telegraphed that he would be met at the Union station, there was a violent denunciation of everyone.

As the Lake Shore train cut off mile after mile, Mrs. Chadwick seemed to realize more fully the serious predicament she was in. She constantly inquired for some information that would tend to show the public sentiment in the city she had called home for so many years. In New York, among strangers, she had not seemed to feel the force of the situation, but Cleveland—that was different! In that city where she had lived in luxury for so long she knew she would have to face her friends.

She was fearful of the ordeal through which she was about to pass and, had she been able, she would have stopped the train long before it arrived in this city. At intervals of fifteen minutes, perhaps to keep up her courage, she would issue bulletins concerning her case. One statement signed by Mrs. Chadwick requested the people of Ohio to suspend judgment to such a time that she might be able to state her side of the case. Then there were more tears.

Five miles from Cleveland she was informed that she was approaching the city. The maid assisted her into a great brown cloak and then tied a heavy brown veil over her face, completely covering it from the view of the public. When the train finally came to a stop in the big, gloomy shed of the Union station, Mrs. Chadwick, leaning heavily on the arms of Deputies Kumb and Kelker, started for the door of her drawing-room. Through the open door she caught a glimpse of the passengers in the sleeper and quickly drew back, declaring that she would not leave the car until it had been cleared.

The passengers stayed in their seats, for they wanted at least one look at the much-talked-about, much-written-about woman. Mrs. Chadwick's apartment was in the rear of the car and she demanded that the rear door be opened so that she might avoid the passengers, but it was said that this was impossible as the door was locked. Reluctantly, she pressed forward, the deputies half carrying her.

The crowd waiting outside seemed inspired not only by idle curiosity, for every time they caught sight of Mrs. Chadwick as she slowly made her way through the car there were jeers and cries of exultation at the sight of the woman in distress. They were savage, fighting and jostling for the best sight of the prisoner. There were no words of pity, but rather a disposition to hit a person when down. . . .

The train was three hours late. It was scheduled to arrive at 11.30 o'clock, but at that time it was announced that it was two hours back. A number of those who were at the station at that time left when their dinner hour had expired, but others came to take their place. Every time the Ashtabula accommodation or any other train from the East pulled into the station, there were shouts of "There she comes!" followed by an outpouring from the waiting rooms and a general scramble to surmount benches to see out over the tracks.

The station really began to look as if something were going to happen at 1 o'clock when Lieutenant of Police Walker marched down with a squad of men, whom he lined up about the carriage entrance to the station, and proceeded to place the station under police ruling. Orders were given that the crowd was to be kept out of this passageway, while the newspaper men would be allowed to the space to the east.

When word was received that the train was running through Collinwood the excitement became intense, and when the snow- and ice-capped train sped into the station it was greeted by a chorus of yells hardly distinguishable between cheers and boos. United States Marshal Chandler was the only one allowed out on the tracks to meet the alighting party. But between the newspaper reporters arriving on the train, passengers on the train, employees at the station, and others who escaped through the lines, there was an amateur mob clamoring about the steps of the vestibule of the sleeping car "Aida" in which Mrs. Chadwick had apartments.

It was several minutes before Freda, the maid, and a couple of newspaper men were seen making their way through the crowd on the tracks. Behind them, coming more slowly, were Marshal Chandler and Deputy United States Marshal Kumb of New York, supporting Mrs. Chadwick between them. The shouts still continued as she came forward, passed the line of police that held back the stationful of curious people, and went out. Without, about the carriages, was another large crowd composed mostly of men and boys, struggling with the police for a glimpse of the most remarkable woman.

Out in the daylight a number of cameras were levelled at her and she made a slight effort to dodge them. It really wasn't necessary, for the day was so dark that there was little chance of clear photographs being taken, especially in the smokiness of the Union station. All this time she leaned heavily on the arms of the federal authorities in whose hands she literally was.

In the absence of the society editors to describe the appearance of one whose costumes they had formerly and under different conditions delineated, it might be mentioned that Mrs. Chadwick wore a brown tailor-made suit, a mauve-coloured raw Shiki silk coat, knee-long, padded with felt and lined with satin. Her hat, too, was brown, empire style, and trimmed with a brown automobile veil draped down doubly thick over her face. She had taken off her heavy cloak and now carried it over her arm.

Marshall Chandler's carriage was opposite the exit, but all about it were crowded the carriages of the newspaper men. Freda and Emil Hoover Chadwick, the son (he had boarded the train at Ashtabula), were left standing in the cold when Mrs. Chadwick was bundled into the carriage by Marshal Chandler. Freda carried a large hat box and other parcels and Emil had a suit case. Two Associated Press reporters took pity on them and invited them into their carriage, and it was in this way that the faithful maid and the devoted son were carried up the hill to the federal building.

The procession drove briskly up Bank street, a *Leader* carriage first, with *Leader* reporters, photographers and messenger boys. Instead of driving around to the front of the building, Marshal Chandler ordered his carriage up Perkins court to the wagon-delivery entrance of the post office. But his carefully laid plans to elude the crowd did not carry well, for the narrow court was filled with coal drays and mail wagons. It was several minutes before the police could clear the alleyway and in the meantime people anxious to see crowded in from every direction. The roofs of the surrounding buildings were occupied, and it seemed to be great sport for the boys up there to throw down huge cakes of snow on the people beneath. A bridge, crossing from one building to another, was flocked with pretty girls, and all the windows in the adjacent buildings were crowded.

Sometimes only moving foot by foot, the carriage neared the door of the federal building, which was manned by guards. Mrs. Chadwick was finally escorted into the building by this door, and the crowd yelled.

By a rear freight elevator she was taken up to the fifth floor, to the rear room of the office of Clerk Carlton of the United

States district court. Freda and Emil were allowed to go up with her. There she met Attorney Sheldon Q. Kerwick, who may defend her, and she was also introduced to District Attorney Sullivan, the man who is prosecuting her. Here, too, she was formally turned over to Marshal Chandler by the Deputy Marshal from New York. She was also re-arrested by Marshal Chandler on a capias based on the indictment returned by the federal grand jury.

No admittance was allowed to the room; police and United States inspectors and secret service men being on all sides. Secret service men came on the train from New York and United States inspectors manned the elevators and guarded the stairway and doors of the federal building.

Mrs. Chadwick had reached the federal building at 2.30 o'clock, and it was an hour later that she was conducted back again by the rear entrance to the carriage. There was another delay, then Mrs. Chadwick was helped into the carriage by Marshall Chandler and Deputy Marshal Sampsell. Deputy Marshal Clotiz was seated on the box with the driver and Deputy Marshal Fanning was at the horses' heads, fighting a way through the mob.

The carriage, surrounded on all sides by police, was driven to the county jail, little more than a block away. Here was still another large crowd held well in check by Lieutenant Walker and a guard of police. The carriage was drawn across the sidewalk, up to the very door of the jail. The crowd leaped forward, the police charged it, the newspaper photographers snapped their cameras, and Mrs. Cassie L. Chadwick was bustled into the Cuyahoga jail to be the guest of hospitable Ed Barry, who entertains perhaps more than any other man in Cleveland.

CHAPTER ELEVEN

C assie went on trial on March 6, 1905 in the courtroom of Federal Judge R. W. Taylor. Public interest in the proceedings was so high that Deputy Marshals had to clear a path for him through the crowds surrounding his chambers.

Among the spectators in the courtroom was Andrew Carnegie. While he stared with obvious interest at the woman who had claimed to be his daughter, he did not speak to her nor did she make any attempt to speak to him.

During a recess, a reporter got close enough to ask him if he was planning to prosecute Mrs. Chadwick himself.

The wiry Scot smiled his rare, thin smile. "Why should I?" he shrugged. "Wouldn't you be proud of the fact that your name is good for loans of a million and a quarter dollars, even when someone else signs it? It is glory enough for me that my name is good, even when I don't sign it. Mrs. Chadwick has shown that my credit is A-1."

The trial lasted six long days. At the end of each day's hearings Cassie was taken back to her cell, for she had refused to apply for bail. Indeed, in view of the public excitement and the seriousness of the charges, it is possible that her lawyers had counselled her against asking for what might not be granted.

In any case, she could not have gone back to Euclid Avenue, for the house had been taken over by her creditors and, pending an auction that was being organized, it was open to the public. People were streaming through at fifty cents a head to gape at the marvels inside. To quote the press:

> Guides usher the daily processions over two-thousand dollar rugs in rooms lined with costly tapestries, a wealth of mahogany, extravagant bric-à-brac, pretentious paintings and statuary, rare books, awe-producing cut glass, awe-inspiring china, antiques and tasteless knickknacks . . . The $9,000 organ produces the music of the masters but no hand is at the keys; a mechanical player has been installed.

The man who might have played it best was still in Europe with his daughter. Cassie said that he was ill at Carlsbad. Certainly, reading the papers, he must have been ill at heart as the trial went on.

Testimony was piled on testimony. Newton, Reynolds, Livesey, and a dozen more. Handwriting experts supported what Carnegie had said; his name on the bottoms of the notes had not been written by him. Some witnesses said that Cassie had worked her way through using hypnotism (there were many references to the effect of looking into her eyes);

others said that this was nonsense and that she was simply a charlatan. The question of whether she was also Madame Lydia DeVere came up, and while the jury was left with the impression that Cassie and Lydia were indeed one and the same, the prosecution did not feel that it needed to pursue this angle in order to get a conviction.

A rumor circulated that on her famous trip to the Carnegie mansion with Livesey, the envelope she brought out had been under her coat when she went in, and that she had spent her twenty minutes inside the house asking to speak to the housekeeper so that she could check a reference that a maid had given her.

Words were piled on words. Whatever the drawbacks of being a juror in those days, one could at least count on being exposed to a high level of eloquence.

On the final day, Cassie's lawyer, Jay P. Dawley, began his summation to the jury by saying, "Here on this beautiful spring morning, when the very elements seem to be arguing with more than moral eloquence on this woman's behalf, survey the pitiful scene before you.

"A woman stands alone on one side and arrayed against her are all the forces of the great, the powerful, the magnificent United States government, the strongest, the mightiest, and the most feared government in the world—and this tremendous, crushing power stands as the accuser of this one weak woman . . ."

Not to be outdone, the United States District Attorney, John J. Sullivan, beating the table with his fist and making the rafters ring with his voice, cried, "I shall not do violence to your intelligence! I have studied you, but if I knew human nature as well as she I would know you all. Perhaps the charm of Cassie Chadwick over men has not ceased. Perhaps the seduction of her smile, the music of her voice, the witchery of her eyes—these things of the enchantress—are with her still to influence some of you. I only hope that you are beyond the powers of this Duchess of Diamonds, this Peeress of Criminality.

"I say that you have before you a crime which for conspicuousness, magnitude, and danger was never exceeded in the annals of the country. You have before you the most dangerous criminal in the world today!"

It took the jury five hours to recover from the rhetoric. Most of the spectators had grown tired and gone home by the time the twelve good men and true (eleven farmers and a real estate man) filed back into court. Andrew Carnegie had remained, sitting by himself, reserved, yet alert. Emil sat by his mother, waiting it out with her.

When the verdict of guilty was announced by the foreman, Cassie, because of her hearing problem, was the only one in the courtroom who did not understand it. Emil put his arm around her shoulder and whispered in her ear. Immediately, her head sank and tears welled in her eyes. It was as though she had really expected to be forgiven. Emil passed her his handkerchief but the flow kept coming and soon she was weeping like a child.

She was sentenced to ten years. Shortly after the trial she was transferred from the county jail to the familiar surroundings of the Ohio State Penitentiary.

CHAPTER TWELVE

Getting settled in her new quarters took time. It was a nice cell, as cells go, although Betsy did wish that the window was lower. It was tiresome having to stand on the toilet bowl whenever you wanted to see out. However, the room was big enough so that Emil could bring in her favorite chaise longue and a couple of chairs. With a Paisley shawl draped over the bowl and a small Turkish rug on the floor, the cell began to feel quite homelike.

The matron, who was as fond of money as anyone, also allowed her to install a small wardrobe in which to keep her things, for it was certain that she wasn't going to receive visitors in the standard prison garb.

And what a number of callers there were! Emil and Freda came every day, of course. Good old Charlie Beckwith also appeared from Oberlin whenever he could, despite the fact that she had caused his bank to close its doors. In addition, there seemed to be an endless supply of lawyers who wanted to talk with her on behalf of their clients; and people who were convinced that, if she would, she could tell them where to find at least a dollar out of each million that had disappeared.

And reporters. Oh, the reporters! They wouldn't let her alone. She sat by the hour on the chaise longue, her silk dress draped over her outstretched legs with only her little polished shoes showing, and parried their questions as she fluttered her ivory fan.

How many millions had she really stolen? Answer: She hadn't stolen a cent. She had *borrowed* a lot, but every business person borrowed. Was she really Andrew Carnegie's illigitimate daughter? Answer: She had never said that she had any claim on him. Well, then, why was he at her trial? Answer: You would have to ask him. Where was all the money now? Answer: Would you like to search the cell?

On and on it went. And as it did, the warden prospered, for he had instituted the practice of charging twenty-five cents a visit. Unfortunately, Betsy complained one day about the number of reporters she had to see. It was getting so bad that Freda couldn't get her hair done in the morning before the first one arrived, and tea with her friends in the afternoon was always being interrupted.

Her complaint was voiced, as it happened, when a reporter from the Cleveland *Plain Dealer* was in earshot. He thought it would be of interest to his readers and it was. When the governor of Ohio read the story, he took a dim view of the warden's charging admittance. And the warden, reprimanded and deprived of his little sinecure, immediately cut off all visitors in reprisal. For months even Emil could not see Betsy. She was put to work in the shirt factory and, despite her fame, was treated almost like an ordinary prisoner, although even the other inmates of the women's section seemed to recognize that she was not and never would be one of them.

After a while, it became possible for Emil to get in once a week, and Betsy immediately embarked on a program of letter writing, slipping the letters to him when the matron was earning her pin money by looking the other way.

At first, her letters drew little response but then, as she began to really become insistent, acknowledgments began to filter back.

She needed very badly to have someone on the outside acting on her behalf. Someone who would be strong and forceful. Someone in a position to influence people. Unfortunately, during the long months when the warden had denied her visitors, the one person she felt that she could rely upon, poor old Charlie Beckwith, had died. Leroy had simply disappeared. (She heard that he was in New York where the man who had bought their organ was paying him to play it for the curious.) Emil, now working as a clerk in a store, was too young, too weak and, much as he loved his mother, too interested in being as unobtrusive as possible. Thus the matter had to be handled by mail.

It was really a lot of fun, in a way. Of all the projects she had dreamed up, somehow this appealed to her most. As she sat in the prison shirt factory, feeding the heavy blue cotton through her clacking sewing machine, she went over and over each detail. The funeral of Cassie Chadwick would be the greatest funeral ever.

Betsy had had the foresight to keep some of her jewellery out of the hands of the bailiffs, and she had Emil sell it all now. A few diamonds, a setting of rubies. They brought surprisingly little considering what she had paid for them. Yet it was enough for this last big event.

The funeral had to be held in Canada, of course. It was only right that she should return home at the end. That was the way the story should go. Besides, the alternative was unthinkable, for the best that she could hope for, lacking friends in Cleveland now, was that the prison would consign her to whatever place they used for deceased inmates.

Therefore, the most important thing was to make sure that someone would come down from Canada to claim the body. After a lot of consideration, she decided that Uncle Harry would be the ideal choice.

At first, her letters to him went unanswered. Weeks, then months went by. She had developed a cough that wouldn't go away and there was pain in her chest that told her to hurry. What was wrong with the man?

Finally, she tried a little blackmail. She wrote him one last, long letter. (Since the paper supplied was so blotter-like that tear stains dried out and became invisible, she had to resort to using drops of weak tea.)

Here she was, wrote Betsy, alone and dying and all she wanted was the family's assurance that when she was gone someone—perhaps dear Uncle Harry—would appear and ask for her body so that it would be taken back to Canada for Christian burial. She implored that they not leave her remains to be disposed of by the Ohio State Prison authorities.

She also pointed out that God might be a little confused if they didn't bury her in the Anglican cemetery at Woodstock. It had to be Woodstock. That was really where her career had begun. Besides, the gravestone was already carved and waiting there. (The stonemason, in acknowledging her payment for it, had assured her that it looked very nice. He had had a little trouble getting the caretaker of the cemetery to let him set it up on the plot she had bought. Tradition demanded that first you buried someone, *then* you put up a stone to say who it was. There was no precedent in Woodstock for erecting a stone saying who it was going to be. However, the money her son Emil had sent on her behalf had been sufficient to alter tradition on a one-time basis!)

The important thing, her letter emphasized, was that she wanted to be sure that Uncle Harry was going to show up, and at the right time. If someone didn't appear to take away the coffin an awful lot of people, she hinted, were going to be embarrassed.

That, of course, was why she had chosen Uncle Harry to do the honors. Of all her remaining relatives (in this sense, remaining meant those still willing to admit they were relatives of hers after all the publicity given to her last trial), Harry was the most dependable. Not bright. Dependable. The sort of farmer a cow could rely on at milking time.

She concluded her letter by repenting her sins, describing the horrors of life in prison (her chaise longue needed re-upholstering) and, finally, by making a nostalgic reference to a childhood experience in the family barn which Harry, if he had any wits left, would understand very clearly as a threat to expose him as he had never been exposed before, even in the barn.

It worked. His pencilled assurance, "I wil be ther" was all she needed to make her feel better than she had in days. She had Emil send him some money, a return train ticket, and a black tie.

It was annoying not to know the minister in Woodstock. She had always had a way with ministers. However, her father wrote that he had seen him for her and had given him her list of "Last Wishes" which was pretty well the complete order of service for the funeral as she felt it should be.

Flowers? Well, that would be nice, but she hesitated to go that far on her own. If a reporter got hold of the fact that she had sent herself a wreath, it would certainly read oddly.

She would just have to hope that, despite his age and infirmity, her father would remember that she had asked him to get some.

If only she had been able to have her funeral sooner! These things took time, but two years was absurd!

Finally, however, everything was arranged. The prison records show that Cassie L. Chadwick (née Elizabeth Bigley) died on October 10th, 1907. Four days later, Woodstock, Ontario, Canada, had the most exciting funeral ever. It was, in fact, the biggest civic event since, six years before, the town had been able to prove it had ten thousand inhabitants and thus had been declared a city.

The principal difference between the two events, the birth of the city and the burial of the best-known former resident of that part of Ontario, lay in the attention drawn from outside the city's limits. While the former achievement was the occasion for expressions of local pride and satisfaction, particularly for those who in the most real sense had been the city fathers, very little attention was paid to the change in status by other parts of the province of Ontario, let alone the world. In contrast, when word went out on the telegraph system that the famous Cassie Chadwick was coming to town, albeit boxed, reporters began to arrive from all over North America. And for the first time the citizens of Woodstock saw newsreel cameras.

To those visitors who inquired in advance, the city promised to be well-equipped to handle the influx. Despite its size, it boasted twelve hotels. Unfortunately, those arriving soon discovered that only two of these catered to transient trade. The rest were, at best, boarding houses operating because the law prevented the government from issuing a licence to sell liquor to anyone who didn't offer sleeping and eating facilities. However, the army of the press marched on its stomach with beds less important than bars, and soon their foremost needs were filled.

When the train bearing the coffin pulled into the station, the reporters, unsteady from waiting at the boarding houses, were almost toppled by the press of people at the tracks. Not since King George and Queen Mary, as the Duke and Duchess of York, had made a whistle stop in Woodstock had so many people turned out to stare.

When the door of the baggage car slid open and Uncle Harry, riding with the coffin, saw the crowd, only the fact that there was no other exit kept him from bolting.

It had been an unnerving experience all the way for Harry. It wasn't just that wearing a tie for three days had almost done him in. Nor was it the fact that he felt he had been rather brusquely handled at the prison, where the simple coffin was waiting for him closed and sealed, and he had had to sign for it as if it were a parcel from Eaton's mail order service. It was, above all, that he had never before travelled further than his horse would take him between feedings. All that time on the trains, sitting in cramped quarters or trying to eat moving soup, had gotten to every aspect of his digestive system. He was approaching the Anglican service in the mood of Calvin.

Strong and almost eager hands helped him slide the coffin out onto a wagon and from thence into the black, rubber-tired hearse that his brother, Dan, had hired. No one had thought to provide conveyances for the mourners, but this was only a minor problem for there were only Harry and Dan and they could walk. Emil, the press was quick to note, had not come along. Betsy's mother had died recently, and the famed woman's brothers and sisters had chosen to wait at the church.

As the cameramen turned their cranks, shooting footage

that a few weeks later would silently flicker down the screens of nickelodeons all over North America, still photographers ran after the hearse pursued by their assistants.

This rather unnerved the funeral director's horses who, tossing their black-pompommed manes, at one point threatened to break into a run and were restrained only by the special whipple tree between them which changed their opinions quickly if they tried to move forward on their own. (The undertaker had invented this device himself and, inadvertently anticipating future devices of analogous effect, called it his gallop pole.)

Like his horses, the driver of the ornate black wagon with its draped glass windows was nervous. Not only was he unaccustomed to the crowds that kept pace with his vehicle, but he was worried because the coffin wasn't behaving itself. All the coffins he had known before, when slipped onto the floor rollers, stayed in place for the duration of the slow journey. But even on the main street, which was about as smooth as a road could be unless you paved it, this coffin tended to slide a bit. Sitting up on his high seat, the driver could feel the occasional bump as the box moved forward on the rollers, hit the front end of the hearse and then slid back. "Damn light coffin!" he muttered, glancing out of the corner of his eye to see if any of those walking alongside had noticed it through the windows.

Apparently the restlessness of the remains went unseen, for he heard no comment. Nonetheless, he was glad when they got to the church and the pallbearers took over.

Dan Bigley had summoned some of his fellow retired railway workers to join him in Woodstock to carry his daughter's coffin. They approached the job of removing it from the rear of the hearse with all the experience of years of lifting rails. It was beautiful to watch as, three on each side, they worked in perfect unison, the scene marred only by the leader crying, "Alley-oop!" at the start. Their march down the aisle of the crowded church was properly in step, and they placed the coffin at the foot of the chancel steps as neatly and exactly as any rail had ever been laid. Then they retired to the second-from-the-front pew and rested for the trip to the graveyard out back.

The minister came in and mounted his eyrie under the great, spreading brass eagle. "What a wondrous thing God hath wrought!" he exclaimed to himself as he looked out over the pews which, for the first time in his ministry, were all filled. "Sin hath its recompense," he thought and then frowned, because while that sounded Biblical it didn't sound quite right. "I wonder where I got that one?" he said to himself as he opened his Book of Common Prayer and flicked through it to the section that told him what to say at funerals.

Normally, his opening of the book was the signal for his congregation to stop murmuring and shuffling their feet and get down to business. Today, however, the crowd before him was not his own. The newspaper people and townsfolk who had crowded in continued to whisper. He looked up, peered at them in the flickering light of the newly-installed electric lamps and tried a cough to get their attention. It didn't work.

"Dearly beloved," he said. Some still talked, their eyes moving constantly to the coffin. "My dear friends," he tried again, a little louder. That helped a bit.

"Cassie Chadwick is dead," he announced. This belated news bulletin caught their attention. The voices were stilled. The eyes swung his way.

"Cassie Chadwick is dead," he repeated, "and we who remain are gathered here today before God to say a last, sad farewell and to commend her to her Maker. Let us begin."

He cleared his throat and plunged into reading the familiar words of the Order for the Burial of the Dead. "I am the resurrection and the life, saith the Lord . . ." It's odd there are no flowers, he thought. Even some wild ones would have been nice. ". . . In my Father's house are many mansions . . ." I wish I could have seen the Chadwick mansion in Cleveland. According to the papers it was some place! ". . . We brought nothing into this world and we carry nothing out . . ." He glanced at the bare brown coffin. From all I've heard, he thought, I wouldn't put it past her to try.

His voice rolled on in the sonorous cadence he had long ago learned. "Therefore, my beloved brethren, be ye steadfast, unmoveable, always abounding in the work of the Lord, forasmuch as ye know that your labor is not in vain in the Lord." He paused. The book said that it was time for a hymn. Referring to his notes, he announced, "Hymn Number One Six Six. Let us sing the first and third verses."

The congregation, being of mixed backgrounds, was uncertain whether to stand or remain seated. The sitters won. Those who had stood at his announcement looked around a little uncomfortably and dropped back into place. In the meantime, the boy working the pump behind the organ got the air pressure up and the music began.

> "Jesus calls us; o'er the tumult
> Of our life's wild restless sea,
> Day by day his sweet voice soundeth
> Saying, 'Christian, follow me!'
>
> Jesus calls us from the worship
> Of the vain world's golden store,
> From each idol that would keep us,
> Saying, 'Christian, love me more.'"

A few of the faithful sang the "Amen." Silence once again descended. The minister looked out over the heads below. Some may have thought he was seeking inspiration. Actually, he was looking at the narthex doors to make sure his bishop hadn't come in, for he was about to commit a sin. At the request of the famous lady whose coffin had come all the way from Ohio, he was about to depart from the script.

He had in his hands what could best be described as a eulogy. It had arrived in the mail a few days previously with a request from Mrs. Chadwick that it be read. At first, he had demurred. Praise for the dead was not too out of place. But when the late departed had gone to her reward from a prison cell in which she had been cloistered for crimes of a rather large order, praise seemed a little out of place. And when one added the fact that she herself was the author of the piece, it made the request additionally odd.

However, the minister had a long-standing respect for last wishes. And since some of her other requests, such as that the town band be employed instead of the organ, were beyond his power to either grant or swallow, he had decided to give in at least on this.

"I would now like to depart from the Order of Service for a moment if I may, to say something about our late friend, Cassie Chadwick, or as we who knew her before her marriage called her, Betsy Bigley." He peered at the sheet of coarse paper in his hand and began to read. "Sir Samuel Cunard once said, 'It is the ship that stays afloat that gets to port.' When Betsy Bigley set sail on life's stormy seas, she little realized how rough the voyage was going to be. Many times as she was buffeted by circumstance and blown off course by man's cupidity, she wished she had never left the safe berth of her Ontario home. It was not easy for an innocent girl to go out into the cruel world alone and unguarded. As we today look back over her voyage, we can see that it really wasn't the pleasure cruise that some have painted it. Nor was she the pirate others have claimed.

"Today, as we gather here to say our last farewell, if there are any who have rancor in their hearts, let it be for Cassie Chadwick, not Betsy Bigley. And if there are any here who still have some love and affection, let it be for Betsy. Cassie Chadwick is dead. Cassie Chadwick will never be seen again. But perhaps those who have loved her and those who have cared will, at least in their hearts, keep Betsy alive."

He glanced at the audience. I'm not too sure what all that means, he thought, but even if I didn't understand it, I read it well, and that is what makes me a good minister. He groped for his book and hurried back into the security of the Order's comforting words. "I heard a voice from heaven saying . . ."

When he came to the Apostle's Creed he was reassured to hear a few of those below saying it with him, even though there was also a rustle of pages turning as others, strangers to the Anglican ritual, flipped through the books they held, trying to catch up. And he distinctly heard one whiskey-roughened voice whisper, "Where the hell is he now?" But it was not a day for hesitation. He swung into the Lord's Prayer and got quite a few approving Amens for that. For the versicles which followed, he made a point of reading the responses as well, if only to keep the thing going. At last the indoor part of the service ended. He moved down to the coffin to read the benediction and then waited as the railway-men filed out of their pew, its door creaking loudly as each man pushed through. (Too bad the front pews don't get used more, the minister thought. The doors on the ones at the rear hardly squeak at all.)

Out of deference to the hallowed hall, the self-appointed foreman refrained from his "Alley-oop!" and merely grunted his cue to lift. There was a moment of slight confusion when the pallbearers, who had lined up facing the chancel, realized that that meant they'd have to walk backwards down the aisle. However, without dropping the coffin, they managed to change hands and get turned around. Then the slow exit began to the organist's rendition of "The Last Rose of Summer"—the minister's final concession to Betsy's requests.

When the procession had worked its way out into the sunlight and round the church, past the carriage shed with its warm odors of horsepower, and into the little graveyard, the minister was relieved to see that there, at least, someone had thought to contribute flowers. Piled around the gravestone were bunches of wild roses.

It was the first time he had ever known a gravestone to be erected before the funeral. Somehow, the roses made it look better. A photographer, eager to get a picture of the stone, pushed some of the branches aside but still the cold grayness of the big square slab seemed less prominent because they were there.

Dan Bigley, standing beside the minister, muttered, "She always liked roses. Was always bringing them home to her mother. I got what I could of what's left on the hedges now."

The minister nodded approvingly and opened his book to continue the Order. It was difficult to concentrate, not only because of the crowd but also because of the strange, whirring sound that came from the cranking newsreel cameras. The picture-taking made him very uncomfortable. He was not a terribly vain man but he did have a frustrating urge to check the white tabs of his clerical tie. This he could not do while holding his book open in the approved manner. Nor could he do much about the way the wind was ruffling his hair. He plowed on to the end and then watched with relief as the cameras on their big, wooden tripods pivoted away from him to film the lowering of the coffin.

No sooner had the coffin reached the bottom of the hole and the ropes gone slack than a cameraman stopped cranking and came over to him. "Excuse me, parson," he said politely, "I know this is a big thing to ask but—well, I ran out of film back there before the coffin was all the way down. Do you suppose the guys on the ropes could raise it a bit and let it down again for me?"

The minister stared at him in disbelief. "This is a funeral," he finally managed to say. "Not a motion picture. Not a motion picture," he repeated, his voice rising. Some of the people heard him and turned toward them.

He glared around. The neat gravel walks could not contain the crowd; people were standing on the graves. Some of the gawking children had actually climbed up on the gravestones in order to see.

How much could he stand? The instructions that had come from the deceased, save for that eulogy and that unfortunate song, he had disregarded. The crowd that came not to mourn but out of curiosity, he had put up with that. But now that the service was over and the coffin had at last disappeared into the ground, to be asked to bring it back up again so that that invention of the Devil could photograph it some more was beyond his capacity to handle.

"Go on with you!" he cried brusquely, giving the cameraman a reproving shove. Unfortunately they were both standing on the loose, freshly-dug earth. The cameraman stumbled, began to slide and then, his balance lost, fell, arms and legs flailing, into the open grave to land with a hollow thud on the coffin.

It made a great scene when it was shown in the motion picture houses. Those who travelled to the nickelodeon in nearby London to see their city on the silver screen were less than pleased with the minister when they got back, for the laughter in the audience as the cameraman, begrimed and obviously swearing, emerged from the grave, seemed somehow to be laughter at Woodstock's greatest moment.

Shortly after, the bishop moved the minister to another parish. However, even there and until his death he was known not so much for his good works and well-read services as for being the minister who had buried Betsy Bigley and, in what seemed an almost symbolic gesture, had tossed in a newsreel man for good measure. It was more than Betsy could have dreamed of.

With this last, unexpected fillip our story ends. There have been rumors that the sealed coffin Uncle Harry accepted at the penitentiary was empty, that Betsy had somehow managed to escape and lived out her remaining days in freedom. We do not know. All that seems certain is that by now—temporarily at least—Betsy's to heaven.